The timid lion

The cunning Kalila and his brother, the compassionate Dimna

The learned physician Burzoe

Kalila wa Dimna

Fables from a Fourteenth-Century Arabic Manuscript

ESIN ATIL

Smithsonian Institution Press
Washington, D.C., 1981

Cover: Fairuz, the Hare, Addressing the Hares (fol. 98a)
Frontispiece: Kalila Visiting the Imprisoned Dimna (fol. 73b)

Library of Congress Cataloging in Publication Data
Main entry under title:
Kalila wa Dimna.
Translation of: Ibn al-Muqaffa''s translation of Kalīlah wa-Dimnah.
Bibliography: p.
1. Kalīlah wa-Dimnah. I. Ibn al-Muqaffa', d. ca. 760. II. Atıl, Esin. III. Title.
PJ7741.B5E3 1981 891'.23 81-607053
ISBN 0-87474-216-1 AACR2
ISBN 0-87474-215-3 (pbk.)

Contents

The author of the book had four objectives in mind when he composed the work:

to render it attractive to the young reader by employing birds and animals in the stories

to capture the attention of rulers by the conduct of the animals who are faced with similar dilemmas and circumstances

to provide entertainment to all peoples and to arouse their curiosity, thereby enabling the book to be preserved through the ages

and to provide the philosophers of the future a forum for discussion and speculation.

Ibn al-Muqaffa

Foreword

The *Kalila wa Dimna,* one of the most popular books in the ancient world, has the same relevance today as it did some two thousand years ago. The fables included in the book express man's relentless battle for survival and expose his frailty as well as his strength. By employing a variety of creatures—such as the lion and the ox, the monkey and the tortoise, the mouse and the cat—the stories explore the consequences of jealousy and pride, trust and deceit, friendship and enmity that constitute the essence of human behavior regardless of time and place. Even though the lessons derived from the fables are intended to guide rulers, the characters and their dilemmas can be appreciated by people of all ages and traditions.

The universality of the morals presented in the stories accounts for the timeless appeal and worldwide popularity of the *Kalila wa Dimna,* which was translated into numerous Eastern and Western languages throughout the centuries. The extensive pictorial cycles of the Arabic versions visually transport the reader into the world of animals. The most charming illustrations were produced in Egypt and Syria during the Mamluk period.

This study, devoted to an outstanding mid-fourteenth-century Mamluk manuscript owned by the Bodleian Library in Oxford, was conceived as two separate but complementary parts. The first part contains selections from eight chapters, which present the most celebrated protagonists and fables; these stories, adapted from the Arabic text, are retold with the modern reader in mind and illustrated with paintings from the original work. The second part traces the history of the *Kalila wa Dimna* and its importance in Islamic literature and art and analyzes the pictorial cycle of the Bodleian manuscript.

I would like to acknowledge the curators of the Bodleian Library, who gave me permission to study and publish the manuscript in their collection. I am particularly grateful for the gracious assistance of A. D. S. Roberts, Keeper of Oriental Books, and Victoria Tandy and Colin Wakefield, assistants in the department.

Amal Abu'l-Hajj (Hull), formerly Curator of the Islamic Museum of the Haram al-Sharif in Jerusalem, translated the difficult passages referred to in the selected stories.

The publication was made possible by a generous grant from the National Committee to Honor the Fourteenth Centennial of Islam and the King Faisal Foundation. I owe a special thanks to the Honorable William R. Crawford, Executive Director of the National Committee, for his encouragement, interest, and support of the project.

Esin Atıl
Curator of Near Eastern Art
Freer Gallery of Art

Introduction

The history of the *Kalila wa Dimna,* also called the *Fables of Bidpai,* is as fascinating as the stories included in the book. The original work, written in Sanskrit, was a compilation of parables taken from the Indian classics. The title is derived from a corruption of the names of the two jackals, Karataka and Damanaka, who are the protagonists of the first story. The book, thought to have been written down around the year 300 by an unknown Vishnuite Brahman living in Kashmir, was later attributed to an Indian sage named Bidpai. It was intended to instruct princes and contains several chapters, which teach a particular moral principle or rule of conduct.

Each chapter begins with the king asking the philosopher the consequences of a certain mode of behavior; the philosopher explains the effects of such an action and illustrates his advice with stories enacted by animals who are caught in a similar predicament. A chapter encompasses a number of parenthetical episodes, tales, sayings, and discourses that emphasize the moral of the story. The animals used in the tales display the full range of human emotion and thought; they speak and behave as if they are living in human societies and are punished or rewarded for their actions.

Although the significance of the work lies in the moral lessons taught by these tales, the didactic theme is often overshadowed by the personalities of the animals who solve their problems with cunning, wit, and ingenuity. The reader tends to remember only the fables, and the fact that these are stories told by the philosopher to the king to illustrate an ethical question becomes a secondary element. Yet this feature is of great structural importance since it provides coherence to the book and links the otherwise independent chapters with each other.

The *Kalila wa Dimna* was introduced to the Near East in the middle of the sixth century. The book was brought from India to Iran by a physician named Burzoe, who had been requested by a Sasanian king to translate the text into Pahlavi (Middle Persian). Burzoe's version was rendered into Arabic by Abdallah ibn al-Muqaffa two hundred years later. Ibn al-Muqaffa's *Kalila wa Dimna* was exceedingly popular and it became the source for subsequent translations. Many later Arabic, Persian, and Turkish renditions were profusely illustrated in the Islamic courts throughout the Near East.

The copy in the Bodleian Library in Oxford, completed in 1354, is among the earliest illustrated Arabic versions of the work. Its anonymous painter invites us to enter a world of fantasy where human emotions, attitudes, and ideas are expressed by anthropomorphic creatures who have established highly structured societies. The individuals inhabiting the sky, sea, and land are as believable and real as the men and women included in the stories. In fact, the human figures, who are represented in a stylized manner, frequently converse with the animals and are a part of this fantastic world, thus prohibiting us from differentiating between man and beast.

The behavior of the animals reflects human weaknesses and strengths, ambitions and achievements. We can relate to the justice and injustice of their world and to the cruelty and kindness shown by friends and enemies since we face similar circumstances in our own lives. We are touched by their endearing personalities; we appreciate their intelligence, resourcefulness, and compassion.

This psychological rapport between protagonist and reader is immensely enhanced by the illustrations, which with their simple compositions, abstracted settings, and charming character portrayals visually transport us into the world of animals.

The *Kalila wa Dimna* is more than a book of parables or a mirror for princes. It symbolizes man's search for truth and justice, challenging his perception of reality on the one hand and the extent of his imagination on the other. The underlying theme of the work is that all creatures, big or small, are a part of creation and each society is a microcosm of a much larger entity that controls the destiny of its members. This perhaps was the essence of the worldwide popularity of the *Kalila wa Dimna,* appealing to all peoples at all times.

Kalila wa Dimna
Selected Stories

The Mission of Burzoe

Nushirvan, the Sasanian king of Iran, was a learned man interested in philosophy. During his inquiries into various sciences, he was informed of a book preserved in India that contained instructions and rules of conduct for princes and kings. It had been written by Indian philosophers and included tales and stories about animals.

The king directed Buzurjmihr, his minister and advisor, to find someone who could procure the book for him. This person had to have literary abilities, a zeal for knowledge, and proficiency with the languages of Iran and India. Buzurjmihr immediately started searching for such a man and eventually found a physician named Burzoe who had the required qualifications.

Burzoe was sent for and presented to the king. Nushirvan told the physician that he was chosen for the mission because of his reputation for wisdom and learning and for his thirst for knowledge; the physician was to go to India to seek the book, which was preserved in the imperial library. Burzoe was to obtain this book at any cost and acquire other Indian writings not known to the Iranians. He was to have all the money he needed for the mission. Nushirvan ordered the astrologers to fix an auspicious date for Burzoe's departure and gave him twenty thousand purses of money, each purse containing ten thousand gold coins. The physician made hasty preparations for his long journey and departed on the day recommended by the astrologers.

After journeying for ten days the physician reached India. He began to frequent the markets and meet important persons, gaining their confidence by telling them that he was a stranger seeking knowledge and in need of their assistance. Thus he made many friends and became intimate with philosophers as well as men of every class and profession. Among his friends was an Indian sage who eventually became his confidant. Burzoe had come to respect and trust this person and told him the secret of his mission.

The Indian answered that he had known all along that Burzoe was hiding the real purpose of his trip, but since he admired the physician's wisdom and understanding, his courteous and affable behavior, and his prudence and perseverance, he would help the physician. The sage warned that this was a dangerous task and if the king of India ever discovered that Burzoe had obtained the book, the physician would be harshly and severely punished. Burzoe assured his friend that his assistance would be kept confidential and that he would leave the country as soon as he had translated the work.

The Indian, convinced of Burzoe's honesty and fidelity, brought to

Burzoe Traveling to India
Burzoe, attended by two courtiers, is embarking on his mission to India. The bearded physician, attired in a white turban with one edge flowing down his back and a golden robe, rides a white donkey; his attendants, dressed in white turbans and blue or red robes, are mounted on horses. The men have golden halos around their heads; Burzoe's halo is enhanced by an additional scalloped border. The riders are placed within a landscape indicated by a ground line of thick green grass, a cluster of leaves, and two large branches laden with buds and blossoms. Burzoe is apparently being escorted to the Iranian border wherefrom he is to travel alone to India.

Burzoe with the Indian Sage
Burzoe and the Indian sage are seated on cushions placed on a rug below an arch with crenelations and triangular projections on the top. A stemmed bowl heaped with food appears in the background. The disguised physician is clean shaven and wears a white turban and blue robe embellished with gold. His confidant is attired in a mauve loincloth with a large golden cloak thrown over his shoulders and knotted below the neck. The Indian, portrayed as a bearded dark-skinned man with long hair, wears gold armlets, bracelets, and belt. Burzoe is explaining the mission entrusted to him by his king and the Indian is warning him of the hazardous consequences if he is caught obtaining the sacred book.

him the book together with other valuable texts kept in the king's library. The physician labored night and day translating these manuscripts from Sanskrit into Pahlavi, in constant fear that the king of India might ask for them before he was finished. He finally concluded his work and sent word to Nushirvan that he had accomplished the mission. Nushirvan ordered him to return as quickly as possible and Burzoe immediately departed from India.

Upon arriving at Nushirvan's court in Iran, the physician presented his translations to the king. The king, seeing that Burzoe was on the verge of collapse from his exhausting work and strenuous journey, ordered him to rest for several days. On the seventh day Nushirvan summoned his amirs and scholars; when they were assembled, he asked Burzoe to read aloud the contents of the book. Everyone was impressed with the profundity of the lessons and the beauty of Burzoe's translation; they showered the physician with their congratulations and expressed their gratitude for the service he had rendered to his country. Nushirvan commanded that the most precious gems of his kingdom, together with all the money in his treasury, be placed before Burzoe. He demanded that the physician sit on a throne like his and put on a crown, thus exhalting him above all the nobles of the land.

Burzoe knelt before Nushirvan and praised his king. He said that since it was the wish of his sovereign that he choose something, he would obey. The physician went to the royal wardrobe and took one of the king's robes. Then he prayed for the glory and happiness of Nushirvan and begged that the king ask Buzurjmihr, the minister, to write a short account of his life and activities and insert it into the book before the chapter on the lion and the ox.

The king replied that it was the least he could do and asked Buzurjmihr to write Burzoe's biography. The minister thanked the king for his confidence and retired to work on the life of Burzoe.

Buzurjmihr began the biography with Burzoe's early schooling, described the physician's first journey to India for the purpose of increasing his knowledge of chemistry and medicine, mentioned his efforts to learn the language of that country, and ended with the mission entrusted to him by Nushirvan. He also included praises of Burzoe's qualities and personal achievements. When the biography was finished, he presented it to Nushirvan. The king assembled his court and requested that Buzurjmihr read it aloud in the presence of Burzoe. After the biography was recited, Burzoe thanked the minister and the king for the honor conferred upon him and his family.

العلماء والرؤساء والاشراف والسوقة فحضروا وحضر برزويه وامر بزرجمهر
ان يقوم قايما فيقرا ما صنع والف على كافة من حضر فقام بزرجمهر على منبر
عال على الناس وقرا عليهم باب برزويه فلما فرغ منه عجب الملك من ذلك وجميع
من حضر مما صنف بزرجمهر من فضل وعقل وادب وعلم وكمال وما اجتهد فيه من مدح برزويه

Buzurjmihr Reciting the Biography of Burzoe

Buzurjmihr, mounted on a dais placed outdoors, is presenting Burzoe's biography to a group of courtiers. The minister, attired in a mauve turban and green robe, stands barefooted on a platform elevated by three steps. Three courtiers, attired in gold, red, or blue, sit on a carpet under the shade of a tree. They listen intently to Burzoe's fascinating life story, expressing their amazement and admiration.

The Lion and the Ox

Dabshalim, the king of India, asked his minister and advisor, who was a philosopher, to tell him stories that contained instructions on governing his kingdom. His first request to the philosopher was to explain how a false and cunning person can come between two friends and cause dissension, turning their love and trust to hatred and enmity.

The philosopher began by telling the story of the merchant and his three sons.

There was a well-to-do merchant with three extravagant and irresponsible sons. When the sons squandered their father's money, the merchant admonished them and gave the following advice: everyone desired three things in life—ample sustenance, respect, and provisions for life hereafter—which could be obtained through four means—to amass wealth by lawful procedures, put this wealth to good use, care for one's own interests, and be generous to the less fortunate.

The sons followed their father's counsel, and the oldest set out on a trading venture with a wagon drawn by two oxen called Shanzabeh and Banzabeh. When they reached a marshy terrain, Shanzabeh, exhausted from pulling the heavy wagon, got stuck in the mud. The young merchant, who was in a hurry, decided to leave the ox with an attendant assigned to free the animal. The attendant waited for a while and then left the ox. When he caught up with his master, he lied and said that the ox had died.

Meanwhile Shanzabeh was able to free himself from the marsh. He found a good pasture near a stream and soon recovered his strength and became fat and healthy. Although he had plenty of food and water, Shanzabeh was lonely. He would bellow pathetically whenever he felt sad and alone.

Not too far from Shanzabeh's meadow was the court of the lion, which included two jackals, Kalila and Dimna, who were employed at the royal gate. The jackals were crafty and bright as well as wise and learned. Dimna was particularly ambitious and not at all content with his present position. He was constantly on the look out to improve his status and be closer to the king.

Every time the lion heard the ox bellow, he cringed in fright, not knowing who was making this dreadful sound. Ashamed of his fear, the lion hid in his den whenever he heard the noise. Dimna noticed that the lion kept close to his den and rarely ventured far from court. He requested an audience with the king and presented himself. He started telling stories, which put the lion at ease, and quickly won the king's confidence. But as soon as the bellow of the ox was heard, the lion became terrified and confessed that he was afraid of whoever was making this noise. Dimna understood the lion's dilemma and began to tell him the story of the fox and the drum.

A hungry fox was walking through the forest when he heard a deafening sound. It was coming from a large drum suspended from a tree; whenever the wind blew, branches hit the drum, thereby producing a loud noise. The fox followed the direction of the sound and when he saw the drum, he attacked it, thinking that it contained food. When he found nothing inside, he realized that it was the insignificant things that were bigger in size and louder in sound.

Dimna finished the story of the fox and the drum by saying that perhaps the terrible sound disturbing the lion was also from an insignificant creature. He volunteered to go and seek its source.

The lion anxiously awaited Dimna's return. When the jackal came back, he reported that the noise was coming from an ox who was big but lacked the power of the lion; he also said that the lion had no reason to fear this creature. The lion, greatly relieved, asked to see this ox. Dimna went once again to the meadow and told Shanzabeh that the lion, the king of the beasts, summoned him to appear at his court. The ox, alarmed at this request, said that he would go with Dimna, provided the jackal promise that no harm would befall him. Upon being reassured by the jackal, he set out to meet the lion.

After Dimna introduced Shanzabeh to the lion, the king asked the ox how he came to this part of the world. Shanzabeh related the story of his falling into the marsh and being abandoned by his master. The lion invited him to stay at his court and soon a great friendship developed between the two. They roamed the forest, held counsel, and thoroughly enjoyed each other's company.

Dimna became jealous of their friendship and felt that his influence with the lion was quickly being replaced by that of the ox. He decided to resort to cunning and treachery to put an end to this affair. He revealed his intentions to his brother, Kalila, who advised him not to compain since it was his fault that the lion met the ox; besides, Kalila said, these two animals were much stronger than a jackal. Dimna, not convinced that defeat should be his fate, told Kalila several stories proving that strength is no match for cunning.

One of these stories was about the lion and the hare. The lion, a fearsome creature, lived in a forest inhabited by many kinds of animals who were terrified of him. They agreed among themselves

الاسد وكيف ذلك قال دمنه زعموا ان ثعلبا مر باجمة وهو جايع وفيها طبل
معلق بشجرة فكلما مر الريح بالطبل فقرعه قضبان الشجر فيشتد ذلك الصوت فلما سمع
الثعلب ذلك توجه اليه حتى راه ضخما ظن ان ذلك لكثرة لحمه وشحمه فعالجه حتى شقه
فراه اجوف فلما راه اجوف قال ما ادري لعل افشل الاشيا اعظمها جثه وابعدها صوتا
وانما ضربت لك هذا المثل لتعلم ان لو قد انتهى اليك كان اسر مما في نفسك
فان شا الملك فليبعثني نحوه ويقيم بمكانه حتى ارجع اليه ببيان فوافق
صفة غوطة وطبل معلق بشجرة والثعلب قد تعلق

The Fox and the Drum
The fox tears at the drum and, much to his astonishment, discovers that there is nothing inside. The brownish orange animal with a long bushy tail and golden neck springs forward. Balancing on his hind legs, he holds the drum in his front paws while biting its top. The large drum is suspended by ropes from a tree densely foliated with leaves and buds. Its articulated trunk is flanked by clusters of grass; a spray of leaves and buds appears behind the fox.

Dimna with the Lion and the Ox
Dimna is bringing Shanzabeh to the apprehensive lion, who sits on his haunches with his tail between his legs. The king of the animals has a sandy yellow coat with a beige mane. Dimna, painted brownish orange with a golden neck, approaches the lion with ease and confidence, apparently quite pleased with himself. Shanzabeh cautiously keeps a safe distance and stands behind Dimna. The ox has brown horns and black spots on his white coat and wears a gold necklace. The hump in the middle of his back suggests that he is a Brahman bull. A tree with leaves and buds is placed behind Dimna and Shanzabeh, while a larger single leaf grows behind the lion and curves gently over him.

that if they sent the lion one animal each day, he would leave the others in peace and not prey upon them. The lion agreed to this arrangement and every day the animals drew lots to determine which one would be fed to the lion the following day.

One day the lot fell on a certain hare, who was exceptionally clever and had no intention of being the lion's next meal. She devised a plan to trick the lion and asked to be sent to him very slowly so that she would be late for the meal. The hungry lion, annoyed that his food was late, was in an ugly mood. When the hare approached him he wanted to know who she was. She said that she was a messenger; the fat hare sent to him by the animals had been seized by another lion. Furious that his territory was invaded by another lion, the lion asked to see his rival.

The hare took him to a deep well filled with water and told him to look down. The lion did as he was instructed and saw his own reflection together with that of the hare. He thought that he was seeing the rival lion with the fat hare intended for him. He leaped at his reflection to snatch his food, fell into the well, and drowned.

At the conclusion of the story Kalila told Dimna that if he could destroy the ox without harming the lion, then he should do so. But Kalila was worried that the lion would become terribly distressed by the loss of his friend.

Dimna, oblivious to his brother's advice, went on with his plans. He stayed away from the lion for several days. When he finally appeared at the court, the lion asked him why he had been absent. Dimna replied that he had heard dreadful news and could not bring himself to face the lion. After pretending to evade the issue, Dimna announced that Shanzabeh was plotting against the lion. At first the lion refused to believe him, but Dimna was able to convince him that the ox was indeed planning to eliminate the king. The jackal suggested that the lion attack the ox before Shanzabeh had a chance to kill him. The lion said that if the story was true, he would order Shanzabeh to leave his court and expel him from his kingdom. But his suspicion was aroused when Dimna warned him to be cautious if the ox approached with his head held down and horns thrust out.

Dimna then sought out the ox and told him the same story. He tried to convince Shanzabeh that the lion was planning to kill him. When Shanzabeh refused to believe this rumor, Dimna said that he was just as naïve as the honest and trusting camel, and proceeded to tell the story of the lion, the crow, the wolf, and the jackal.

The lion dwelt near a public road and had three companions: the

The Hare and the Lion
The clever hare and the foolish lion are placed at opposite sides of the well, looking down into their respective reflections. The sandy yellow lion stands on rocks over a cave on the right, while the pinkish mauve hare is perched on a tuft of grass on the left. The lion is about to leap into the well and attack what he thinks is his rival; he has one paw already in the water and bends his head down in a posture of attack. The bright-eyed hare is securely seated on her haunches. The articulated rocks are painted in varying tones of pink and orange, and the blue water has decorative patterns outlined in dark blue.

crow, the wolf, and the jackal. The lion hunted regularly and his companions fed well on his leftovers. One day some merchants passing by left behind them a camel, who wandered into the marsh where the lion lived. The lion decided to spare the camel and give him protection since the animal was harmless and ate only grass. The camel joined the other companions and was very happy to be in their company.

During one of his outings, the lion ran into a powerful elephant who attacked him. They fought furiously and the lion was so badly wounded that he crawled back to his home and lay sick for days. He became weaker and weaker, unable to hunt and eat. The crow, the wolf, and the jackal, accustomed to being fed by the lion, could not find food and decided that the easiest catch was the camel. When they told the lion they intended to eat the camel, the lion was indignant; he had promised to protect the camel and would not go back on his word. The three companions then devised a plan to trick the camel. They told him that since the lion was wounded and could not hunt, he was in desperate need of food. They were willing to offer themselves to the lion who had protected and befriended them. First the crow asked to be eaten, but the others objected, saying that he was small and scrawny and could not satisfy the lion's hunger. Then the wolf offered himself, but he, too, was rejected since his meat was indigestible and gave cramps and pain. When it was the jackal's turn, they told him that his flesh was stinking and foul and thus inedible. Then the simple-minded camel said that his flesh was the sweetest and asked that the lion eat him, thinking that the others would make excuses for him as well. But this was exactly what the three companions had planned; they fell upon the unsuspecting camel and tore him to pieces. The lion, seeing that the camel had offered himself willingly and it was now too late to save him, joined the others.

When Shanzabeh heard this story, he wondered whether he would come to a similar end. Dimna continued to persuade the ox that the lion was determined to kill him. The jackal said that if Shanzabeh did not take the advice of friends, his fate would be like that of the tortoise who did not profit from wise counsel.

The tortoise lived in a marsh together with two geese. They were good friends and enjoyed one another's company. But, when the marsh began to dry up, the geese decided to seek another lake to build their nest. The tortoise asked them to devise a plan so that he, too, could go with them and not be left behind to die. The geese

The Lion and the Elephant Fighting
The animals are locked in combat with the gray elephant strangling the lion with his strong trunk; his sharp tusks, smeared with blood, pierce the lion's shoulder. Clawing and biting the elephant's neck, the lion struggles to free himself from this powerful grasp. The elephant, wearing a scalloped gold cap, towers over the lion, his massive form made even more so by his static pose. In contrast, the lion swings his tail, bends and twists under the elephant, displaying a realistic struggle for survival. The outcome of this dramatic battle is indicated by the movement and arrest portrayed in the scene.

The Lion, the Crow, the Wolf, and the Jackal Attacking the Camel
The mauve camel with a gold necklace has fallen on his back, spreading his legs and exposing his tender underbelly; his long neck is contorted and his head is twisted under his body. The lion jumps on the camel, his claws tearing the belly, his jaws clamped on the side; the crow bites the ankle; while the wolf and the jackal attack the neck. The agony of the camel is clearly expressed by the tortured look on his face: his eyes are open wide in disbelief and a cry of horror and pain escapes from his mouth. The cruelty of the slaughter is accentuated by the heartless manner in which the sandy yellow lion, the dark gray and black crow, the brownish orange wolf, and the pinkish mauve jackal fall upon their prey and devour him. A few branches with blossoms and a large single leaf framing the lion appear in the background.

told him that if he took hold of the middle of a stick with his mouth and they held its ends in their beaks, they could transport him. But, they warned, he would have to observe absolute silence during the flight.

The tortoise promised to keep quiet and took the stick in his mouth. The geese began to fly, carrying the tortoise with them. They passed over a group of villagers who were amazed by this strange sight; they began to laugh and make fun of the tortoise. The tortoise forgot his promise and opened his mouth to answer them. He let go of the stick and fell to his death.

Shanzabeh, now totally convinced that Dimna was telling the truth, decided to go to the lion peacefully and affectionately and try to persuade him to change his mind. This, naturally, would have upset Dimna's plans. He told the ox to watch the lion's mood: if the lion's ears were extended like arrows and his paws were stamping the ground, then he was ready for the kill.

Shanzabeh, terrified of the lion, approached him cautiously. The lion saw him coming and became nervous; he extended his ears like arrows and began to stamp the ground with his paws. The ox saw this change in his friend and became even more frightened; he held his head down and thrust out his horns. Things were exactly as Dimna had predicted and each was now sure that the other was out to destroy him. The lion and the ox engaged in a ferocious battle that lasted a long time.

Kalila and Dimna came to see the outcome of this fierce encounter. During the course of the battle Dimna told his brother several stories. Kalila scolded him for breaking up the friendship between the lion and the ox and warned him that if his treachery were ever discovered, Dimna would be severely punished.

Finally the battle was over and the lion had fatally wounded the ox. Soon after Shanzabeh died, the lion repented and missed his friend. Dimna tried to justify the kill by saying that when a poisonous snake has bitten a man's finger or toe, he cuts off his hand or foot so that it does not infect the entire body.

Later the lion learned that it was Dimna's envy and deceit that had caused the death of Shanzabeh. Thus, a lying confidant and a false friend had caused a friendship to be severed and had turned the love between two friends into hatred.

Two Geese Carrying the Tortoise
A pair of blue geese with golden shoulders and beaks fly with the mauve tortoise, who has an orange and golden shell. The geese hold in their beaks a stick; between them is the tortoise biting onto the stick. Below are two barefoot villagers, their arms extended in amazement. One of them is a clean-shaven youth, the other is a bearded man; both are dressed in turbans and robes. Opposite the men is a large tree with pear-shaped blossoms. The geese fly with ease, their swooping bodies and curving necks creating a graceful movement in the sky. The tortoise, unaccustomed to being in the air, looks uncomfortable with tail and feet sticking awkwardly out of his shell.

The Lion and the Ox Fighting
During the course of the battle, the lion jumps on the ox, biting and tearing the animal's hump. Shanzabeh bends his head and thrusts his horns into the lion's chest. They hit one another with such force that both are lifted off the ground with the impact. A few pear-shaped blossoms and sprays of grass cover the ground and two trees with different types of leaves grow in the background.

The Trial of Dimna

Having heard how falsehood and deceit ruined a friendship, the king told the philosopher that he would like to know if Dimna's tricks were discovered and if he was put on trial and punished.

The philosopher replied that Dimna's treachery was discovered by the leopard, who was highly trusted by the king.

Late one night the leopard overheard Kalila and Dimna talking: Kalila was rebuking Dimna for his actions and Dimna had confessed all his wrongdoing.

The leopard immediately went to see the lion's mother and related to her the entire story. She promised to keep the source of this information secret, but as soon as the sun rose, she went to her son. The mother told the lion the story exactly as she had heard it from the leopard without mentioning his name and advised her son to seek the truth.

The lion replied that in his heart he knew that he had wronged Shanzabeh and wanted to know who had discovered Dimna's plot. The mother kept her promise and would not indulge the leopard's name. She said that if she betrayed her informant she would be dishonest, lose his friendship, and no one would ever confide in her again.

After his mother departed the lion called his court together and demanded that Dimna be brought to him. When the jackal arrived, he was told that he was guilty of deceit and wickedness. Dimna, whose cunning was matched by his wit, tried to justify his acts by lengthy declamations. The lion requested that a trial date be set and Dimna be judged by his peers. The jackal continued to plead his case and to overwhelm the lion with clever speeches and philosophical discourses.

The lion's mother, fully aware of Dimna's cleverness and its effect on her son, was very angry at the proceedings and advised the lion to take action and not be dissuaded by Dimna's smooth talk. She had to reveal the name of her informant, the leopard, to convince the lion of Dimna's guilt. The lion, relieved that the informant was the reliable leopard, who he greatly esteemed, had Dimna bound and put in prison until the day of the trial.

Kalila heard that Dimna was in prison and went to see him in the middle of the night so that no one would know of his visit. When he saw Dimna's condition, he was overcome with affection for his brother and tears came to his eyes. He told Dimna that he had

The Lion with His Mother
The lion sits on his haunches on the right, looking rather forlorn and depressed with his shoulders sagging and his tail between his legs. Opposite is the lioness, who has an indignant expression and sits erect with her head held forward. The lion bends his head and turns his ear toward his mother, listening intently to her words. Two branches with blossoms grow behind the protagonists, who are separated by a cluster of grapes.

Kalila Visiting the Imprisoned Dimna
When Kalila visits Dimna at night, he finds his brother chained in an arched enclosure with a triangular projection on the roof. Dimna, painted brownish orange with a golden neck, sits with his tail between his legs with a mischievous look on his face. Kalila, painted mauve with a golden neck, looks at him with a sad and compassionate expression. The spray of leaves and buds behind Kalila forms a contrast to the architecture enclosing Dimna, thereby stressing his confinement. The opposing personalities of the brothers and their attachment to each other are explicitly portrayed.

ruined his life by avarice, greed, and haughtiness, and he wept for his brother.

After Kalila left Dimna and returned home, he felt very sad and troubled. He grieved over his brother's impending punishment; he was afraid that if anyone had seen him visiting the prisoner, they might think that he was a partner in the plot; he also thought that Dimna might try to implicate him to lessen his own guilt.

Poor Kalila was stricken with these thoughts when a severe pain attacked his heart. He gasped for breath and departed from life by a sudden death.

The next day Dimna was put on trial. The judge assembled the king's forces and the commanders of the troops and Dimna was brought before them. The leopard addressed the group, asking the judge to prosecute the culprit. Dimna's cunning was still at work; he told the judge several stories in defense of his actions.

The following day the leopard, the scribes, and the king's forces wrote out the accusations and Dimna's defense and presented both documents to the king. When these were studied, it appeared that Dimna's defense and clever way with words had won over the accusations.

The trial continued for ten days without reaching a verdict. Finally the lion's mother persuaded the leopard to testify. Then a relative of the king came forth and gave testimony that corroborated the leopard's story. This person had seen Kalila and Dimna conversing the night the jackal was imprisoned and related the prisoner's confession exactly as he had heard it. Since the two witnesses agreed, Dimna was brought out of prison and was faced with the truth. He was stunned and could no longer defend himself. The lion ordered him bound in chains and confined to a narrow cell without food or drink. Dimna died of starvation shortly thereafter.

The Ringdove

The king said to the philosopher that now that he had heard the story of the envious and deceitful man who brought corruption among friends, he would like to know how a man is received into brotherhood among his fellows and how strangers of alien races can come to love and trust one another.

The philosopher answered that nothing is equal in value to brotherhood because brothers can help in times of trouble, rescue one another from hidden snares, and protect their kin from enemies, like the crow, the mouse, the tortoise, and the gazelle.

There was a fertile region with abundant grass and trees frequented by fowlers and hunters. An old and wise crow lived in a tree that was particularly large and rich in foliage. One day the crow saw a hunter spreading a net below the tree and covering it with safflower seeds. Soon a flock of doves flew in. Their leader, a ringdove, spotted the seeds but did not notice the net. When the doves landed on the ground to feast on the seeds, the snare was drawn and they were caught in the net.

The ringdove suggested that the group unite and fly away together before they were caught by the hunter. The birds followed his advice, flapped their wings in unison, and took off with the net just as the hunter was approaching.

The crow decided to follow them. The doves flew over hills and houses with the hunter in hot pursuit. They eventually lost the man and landed near a burrow where a mouse lived. The ringdove called her friend, Zirak, the mouse, who came out of his burrow and saw the birds entangled in the net. He began to gnaw the ropes and finally cut through the snare. The doves rejoiced at being freed; they congratulated each other and thanked the mouse before flying off. Zirak returned to his home.

The crow, impressed by the friendship between the ringdove and the mouse, decided to stay on. He called out to Zirak and told the mouse that he would like them to be friends. Zirak, knowing well that crows are the natural enemies of mice, was slightly apprehensive at first but became convinced of the crow's sincerity and accepted his offer of brotherhood. A strong bond soon developed between the two, and they came to rely on one another.

The crow, noticing that their homes were too close to men, suggested that they move to another area. He knew of a secluded region full of vegetation and water where his friend, the tortoise, lived. The mouse agreed and the crow took him by the tail and flew to the

The Mouse Gnawing the Net Imprisoning the Doves

Seven blue and golden doves, caught in a net, are helped by Zirak, a charcoal gray mouse, who has come out of his burrow and is busily gnawing the ropes. Observing this unusual sight is the gray and black crow perched on the branch of a tree growing above Zirak's home. The doves are shown with fluttering wings, accentuating their helpless confinement in the net. Zirak bites intently on one edge of the snare, while the large crow looks down inquisitively.

pond of the tortoise. The three friends enjoyed each other's company and passed their days in peace and happiness.

One day a gazelle came running into their neighborhood and frightened them. The tortoise dove into the water, the mouse scurried into his burrow, and the crow took flight and hid in a tree. When they saw that no one was pursuing the gazelle and that the animal was merely thirsty, they came out of hiding. The gazelle told them that he was running away from hunters. The friends asked him to join them and live in their peaceful place. The gazelle moved in, enjoyed good company and ample food and drink.

It became the custom of the four friends to meet every day, talk about their lives and experiences, and share their meal together. One day the gazelle failed to show up and the crow, the mouse, and the tortoise were worried that some misfortune had befallen him. The crow took to the air, searched for the gazelle, and saw that he was caught in a hunter's net. He reported what he had seen to the mouse and the tortoise, who then set out to rescue their friend. When they reached the gazelle, the mouse began to gnaw the net and eventually freed him. The gazelle turned to the tortoise and said that if the hunter came back, he could run away, the crow could fly, and the mouse could hide; but, the slow and defenseless tortoise would probably be caught. As they were talking, the hunter arrived; the gazelle, the crow, and the mouse ran away and hid, but the tortoise, who could not move fast enough, was captured by the man. The hunter bound him and took him away, slung over his shoulders.

The friends, distressed by the loss of their brother, devised a plan to free him. They decided that if the gazelle pretended to be wounded and lay down with the crow who would appear to lick his wound, they might deceive the hunter. The gazelle followed their plan and lay down in the path of the hunter with the crow over him; the mouse hid nearby and they waited for the man. When the hunter arrived and saw them, he let go of the tortoise and went after the gazelle. The crow took flight and the gazelle jumped up and ran, luring the hunter away from the tortoise. The mouse quickly went to the tortoise and severed the ropes binding him.

By the time the hunter returned, the friends were safely far away. The man was disappointed and ashamed of himself for having lost his catch. He had become quite leery of this region and moved onto another area. The crow, the mouse, the tortoise, and the gazelle rejoiced; they embraced and kissed each other, greatly relieved that now they could live in complete peace and happiness.

The Gazelle with the Crow, the Mouse, and the Tortoise
In the center of the scene is a semicircular pond, its shores lined with grass and pear-shaped blossoms. The pinkish mauve gazelle with black horns and golden neck stands at the edge of the pond with his front legs in the water. He looks up at the crow perched in a tree; directly below is a burrow from which the mouse peers out. The tortoise swims toward the gazelle and speaks to him. The figures and their postures create a circular movement around the pool that is echoed by the landscape elements. This structural device expresses the psychological involvement of the protagonists and reinforces their friendship and interdependence. Each figure is connected to another by the movement of his body and direction of his gaze and by the landscape elements.

The Gazelle Luring the Hunter While the Mouse Frees the Tortoise
Attempting to foil the hunter, the gazelle runs to the left, pursued by the man, while the mouse gnaws the ropes binding the tortoise. The gazelle turns back as he runs, enticing the hunter to follow him. Attired in a white turban and short red robe with gold bands, the barefooted hunter, who runs after the animal, displays amazement at the sudden recovery of the gazelle. On the right is the poor tortoise bound to a stick and cast upside down against a rock by the hunter in his anxiety to catch the gazelle. The mouse scampers over the rock and hurriedly bites the ropes, trying to free the tortoise before the hunter returns.

The Owls and the Crows

The king said to the philosopher that now that he had heard the fable about brotherhood and how friends help one another, he would like to hear a story about an enemy one should never trust even though he appears to be friendly.

The philosopher answered that when a man trusts a cunning enemy, he is bound to have the same fate as what befell the owls at the mercy of the crows.

There was a certain forest with large trees and excellent pastures. One thousand crows and their king had built a rookery in the largest tree. Nearby was a hill where one thousand owls lived with their king. One night the owls attacked the crows without warning; they killed and wounded many crows and departed as suddenly as they had arrived.

After the owls retreated at dawn, the crows assembled around their king. When the king saw how many had been killed, badly wounded, or had a broken wing, he realized that the owls were much stronger and would attack again to finish them off. He asked five of his most learned ministers to find a solution and help him save the remaining population.

The first counselor said that since the enemy was too powerful, they should move far away. The second felt that they should prepare for battle and fight for their lives to the very end. The third disagreed and proposed that they find a mediator and make peace, even if they had to pay a yearly tribute. The fourth believed that they should surrender now, but secretly build up their arms and fight back when they were strong enough. The fifth considered the solutions given and found fault with each. He said that having more than one counselor was detrimental to rulers; a king should have only one advisor who was thoroughly devoted to the sovereign and to the good of the nation.

The king dismissed the group and called the fifth crow to his quarters to discuss the problem. The crow began by telling him the story of the hare and the elephant.

There was a region where many elephants lived. Their lake had dried up and the springs feeding it had disappeared. Suffering from thirst, the elephants gathered together and complained to their king. The king sent out his confidants and secretaries to explore the land and search for water. One of them came back with the news that he had found a lovely place with a clear and pleasant body of water,

The Owls Attacking the Crows
The surprise attack of the owls takes place in the air, above a rocky landscape. Four orange owls with golden eyes hurl themselves at the crows, pecking their defenseless prey. Five other crows are perched in a tree, unaware of the ferocious battle. Articulated rocks are painted in varying intensities of blue, pink, and orange, their calm swooping contours providing a contrast to the flurry of flying bodies. The aggressiveness of the owls and the helplessness of the crows are explicitly portrayed: the owls hover over the crows, biting their heads, necks, and bodies; the crows are overcome by the fury of the attack, unable to fight back. The unexpectedness of the attack is enhanced by the group of sleeping crows perched in the tree.

called the Lake of the Moon. The king moved his herd to this place and the elephants finally had plenty to eat and drink.

This region was inhabited by the king of the hares and his subjects. When the elephants arrived at night, they trampled a number of hares and killed them. The next morning the remaining hares gathered around their king and asked him to devise a plan that would deliver them from the elephants, make them leave the pasture, and save the remaining hares. The king called upon his counselor, a wise and learned hare named Fairuz. Fairuz addressed the group and suggested that he go as a messenger to the elephants and talk to them.

Fairuz set out on a moonlit night to meet the elephants. Afraid that they might not see him and would step on him, he climbed on a rock overlooking the herd and called out to their king. He announced that he was the messenger of the moon. The moon had said that although the king of the elephants boasted of his strength and harmed the weak, his strength would cause his downfall; the king had disturbed the moon's lake and drunk its water wrongly; if he returned to the lake, the moon would blind him and his subjects; and if the king doubted these words, he should come to the lake and find out for himself.

The king of the elephants, curious to meet this powerful moon, set out to the lake with Fairuz. When they arrived, he saw the reflection of the moon in the water. Fairuz told him to pay homage to the moon by drinking the water and washing his face before speaking. The elephant went into the water and did as he was told. He hastily withdrew when he saw the reflection of the moon move; he thought that the moon was trembling in anger and quickly apologized for having entered the lake. He was overwhelmed by the power of the moon and gathered his herd and departed from the pasture, leaving it to the hares.

When the crow finished his story, the king asked him how they could be free from the enmity of the owls. The crow then told him other stories, which proved that a small but clever person could easily overpower a strong opponent with his intelligence. He explained his plan to trick the owls and asked that word be sent out saying that the king was angry with his confidant and counselor; then the crows were to beat him up and pluck his wings and cast him beside a tree; he also told the king to take his subjects and go into hiding.

Fairuz, the Hare, Addressing the Hares
Fairuz explains his plan to a group of four hares surrounded by several blossoming trees. The wise counselor sits quietly on an articulated orange rock overlooking the other hares, his silence accentuated by the disorganized chatter of the group. He is portrayed as a dignified individual whose wisdom and knowledge outrank those of the others.

Fairuz at the Pond with the King of the Elephants
Fairuz watches the king of the elephants entering the lake and seeing the reflection of the moon. The huge gray elephant with a scalloped gold cap has both front feet in the lake and is about to scoop up some water in his trunk when he notices the movement of the moon's image. Fairuz, seated on a rock beneath a spray of large leaves, observes his reactions with interest. Hanging like a canopy over the scene is a deep blue sky with a golden moon.

They did as he requested and when the king of the owls came with his army that night, he found all the crows gone. The only one left was a badly beaten crow crawling on the ground. He questioned the crow, who told him that he had been beaten by his own kind and banished from their society since he had advised his king to surrender to the owls and make peace.

After hearing the crow's story, the king of the owls asked his advisors what they ought to do with him. The first said he should be killed since an enemy can never be trusted; the second advised that he should be treated with compassion; and the third suggested that he should be honored so that he might become loyal and help them later. The king agreed with the advice of the third counselor and ordered the crow fed and his wounds treated. The crow was given the best meats and his needs were attended to without delay. He soon recovered and began to gain the confidence of the owls. He learned their secrets and soon became acquainted with their habits.

When he had acquired sufficient information, he flew back to his companions. He told the king of the crows that the owls lived in a cave that had a small entrance. He asked all the crows to take a piece of dry wood and place it in front of the opening. One of them was to bring a flaming branch and set the dry wood afire. Then, they were to fly in front of the fire and fan the flames with their wings. If the owls came out, they would burn; if they remained inside the cave, they would die from the heat and smoke. The king ordered the crows to do as his counselor planned and the crows returned victorious, rejoicing in the death of their enemy.

After the enemy was eliminated, the king of the crows asked his counselor if he found the owls intelligent, skillful, and prudent. The counselor said that the only intelligent one among the lot was the owl who advised his king to kill the crow. This owl had warned him to beware the enemy and not to trust his friendship, even when he seemed weak and harmless. But the king was foolish and careless; he did not follow good advice and paid dearly for his mistake.

The Crow Talking to the King of the Owls

The cunning crow is brought before the king of the owls, who is attended by his court. The king, with a halo around his head, is perched on a rock and questions the crow who stands submissively before him. Four other owls appear behind the crow and listen to his story. The strong gray and black coloring of the crow distinguishes him from the orange owls and the pink rocks. One senses that although surrounded by enemies, the captive crow, with his individualism and intelligence, will conquer the might of the owls.

The Crows Trapping the Owls in the Cave

The owls are huddled together in a cave while the crows fan with their wings the fire they have started in front of the entrance. Four crows, flying in a diagonal formation, approach the cave, with the first one leading the way and beckoning the others with his wings. The conical cave, painted in varied shades of blue, encloses the owls who are shown as an orange mass with golden eyes. The flames of the fire lit at the mouth of the cave cover its opening, preventing the owls' escape.

The Monkey and the Tortoise

After he had heard the parable of the deceitful enemies and how one should guard against them, the king said to the philosopher that he would like to hear about a man who acquires wealth but does not know how to manage it.

The philosopher replied that acquiring was easier than keeping. The man who amasses wealth without knowing how to manage it is like the monkey and the tortoise. The tortoise had the monkey in his grasp but could not handle him; the monkey slipped away and the tortoise was left with disappointment.

One of the islands in the ocean was inhabited by monkeys. Their ailing and aged king was ousted by an ambitious young monkey. The old king crept away and arrived at a region where there was a pond with plenty of fruit trees growing on its shores. The monkey moved into one of the fig trees and feasted on the fruit. As he ate, he would drop some of the figs into the pond, delighted by the sound they made when they splashed in the water.

One day he saw a tortoise in the pond eating the figs. The tortoise, thinking that the monkey was throwing the figs for him, wanted to become friends with the former king. They started talking and eventually became devoted to one another. Like the monkey, the tortoise was separated from his family, having left his wife and children on another island.

The wife of the tortoise began to complain of her husband's attachment to the monkey and told a friend he was neglecting her because of this relationship. The friend advised her that if the monkey were eliminated, her husband would return. They devised a sinister plan to dispose of the monkey. The wife wrote to the tortoise saying that she was gravely ill. When he came to see her she pretended that she was too sick to talk. Her friend told the tortoise that the only cure for her ailment was the heart of an ape; otherwise, she would die.

The tortoise distressed by his wife's illness and disturbed that the only medicine was his friend's heart, decided that he had to destroy the monkey to save his mate. He planned to take the monkey to an isolated island, leave him there without food or drink until he died, and then remove his heart and give it to his wife.

When he came back to the pond, the monkey inquired about his wife. The tortoise implored his friend to come home with him so that his children might serve him and his wife might recover by his company. He said that his home was in a dense forest with cool

صورة القرد راكب فوق السلحفاه وهي تخوض في النهر

فقال له ما منعك يا خليلي اذ كان الامر على ما ذكرت
ان تكون اعلمتني فاقبل معي بقلبي فانه لا ينبغي ان يمنع الناسك
من التماس الاجر ولا السلطان طلب المنفعة ولا النسا
عطية لتنتفع بها اللذة لانهن قرة اعين الرجال فقال السلحفاه
فاين قلبك يا خليلي فقال تركته في منزلي فقال السلحفاه

The Tortoise Swimming with the Monkey on His Back
The gray monkey wearing a gold necklace sits on the tortoise, who swims in the water. The blue pond, decorated with stylized patterns and framed by grass, is flanked by branches bearing leaves and buds. The monkey, perched precariously on the tortoise's shell, has a worried and preoccupied look on his face as he converses with his friend. The tortoise also looks unhappy and is paddling away slowly.

The Monkey Jumping Safely to the Shore

The monkey, after jumping to the safety of the shore, converses with tortoise. The former king sits in his tree and gestures toward the tortoise, who lifts himself from the water in response. The rectangular pond with stylized waves is framed by grass and two large trees. The amiable exchange between the two former allies indicates that their friendship has not been lost.

waters and delicious fruit. The monkey, lusting after the fruit, agreed to go with the tortoise.

The monkey climbed onto the back of the tortoise, who began to swim toward his home. Lost in thought, he would paddle for a while and then stop. The monkey sensed something was wrong and asked him what was amiss. The tortoise, who had begun regretting his evil plans, confessed that the only cure for his wife's ailment was the heart of an ape. When the monkey heard this, he realized that his life was in danger and tried to find a way out of his dilemma.

The monkey said that he sympathized with the tortoise and knew how precious his wife was to his friend. Their women were also afflicted with a similar disease but recovered when they received an ape's heart. The monkeys were not injured when they gave up their hearts; they were in pain for a while but soon recovered. He said that he would happily give his heart to the wife, except that he left it on the fig tree next to their pond. He suggested that they go back so that he could retrieve it.

The foolish tortoise was so relieved that he did not have to hurt his friend that he gladly brought the monkey back to the pond. The monkey leaped ashore and climbed his tree. When the tortoise urged him to come down, the monkey laughed and accused the tortoise of being a false friend. The tortoise confessed his sins and begged forgiveness.

The monkey forgave the tortoise and said that if the tortoise wished to remain on the island, he would feed his friend as before; but if the tortoise desired to go home, he would wish him peace; and if in the future the tortoise wanted to come back to the pond, he would have the monkey's blessings. Thus parted two old friends and the tortoise went home in humiliation and shame.

The Mouse and the Cat

The king asked the philosopher to narrate a parable in which a man has many enemies who approach him from all sides and yet he manages to escape them.

The philosopher replied that enmity is not always perpetual for sometimes hatred changes into love and love changes into hatred, as in the case of the mouse and the cat.

There was a banyan tree in one of the provinces. Living in a burrow under the tree was a mouse named Faridun and inhabiting a hole nearby was a cat called Rumi. This area was favored by hunters who came frequently to trap the animals. One day a hunter laid out his net near the tree and concealed it with branches and leaves. When the cat came out of his hole to search for food, he fell into the snare. The mouse, who had also come out of his burrow, saw the cat entangled in the net. He looked around and, much to his distress, saw a weasel lurking in the background, ready to attack him; then he looked up and saw an owl perched on a tree, waiting to snatch him. The mouse was afraid that if he turned back, the weasel would kill him; if he climbed the tree, the owl would get him; and if he remained where he was, the cat would find a way to escape from the net and devour him.

Faridun thought for a while and decided that his best chance for survival was to make friends with the cat. He approached the cat and proposed an alliance: he would pretend to be an old friend of the cat and come closer, thereby warding off the weasel and the owl; after these two left, he would free the cat from the net. Rumi agreed to this arrangement. The mouse went up to the cat and they embraced like old comrades, each asking the other how he felt. Then Faridun started gnawing at the ropes to free the cat. The owl and the weasel watched this phenomenal sight in astonishment and then departed.

After the weasel and the owl left, Faridun slowed his gnawing and left one rope intact. But upon seeing the hunter approach, he cut the last thread and ran quickly to his burrow. The cat sprang free from the net and climbed a tree. Thus traditional enemies, who had become friends in times of distress, parted amicably forever.

The Mouse Gnawing the Net Confining the Cat

On the left is the black and white cat with a golden neck, imprisoned in a net. On the right is a light gray weasel emerging from a hole while holding onto Faridun's tail. Above Faridun is a large owl perched on a branch and looking down at the mouse. In the center is Faridun, who has started cutting through the ropes. A triangular formation is created with the cat, the owl, and the weasel at each corner; in the middle is the mouse, who is the natural prey of all three. By this compositional device we are made aware of Faridun's dilemma and the danger of being surrounded by three enemies. The act of the weasel grasping the mouse's tail further stresses Faridun's precarious position.

The Traveler and the Jeweler

The king asked the philosopher to tell him how a ruler can select from a whole group of men one individual upon whom to bestow his favor.

The philosopher replied that kings should give favors to all men but not trust every one. Favors should be granted especially to those who are grateful and appreciative. An intelligent man should not despise or belittle anyone, whether small or great, man or beast; he should test them first and act accordingly. Then the philosopher illustrated his advice with the fable of the traveler.

A jeweler had fallen into a pit someone had dug to catch animals. Then a monkey came by and also fell into the pit. The same happened to a leopard and a snake. Eventually a traveling ascetic approached and decided to help them out of the pit, particularly the man who was trapped with the animals. The ascetic threw a rope down into the pit and pulled up the monkey; then he saved the leopard and the snake. The animals thanked him but warned him not to pull up the jeweler because, they said, no one in the world was as ungrateful as man. But the ascetic felt sorry for the jeweler and pulled him out as well.

The animals wanted to repay the ascetic's kindness and told him where they lived; if he should be in the neighborhood and call upon them, they would be happy to see him. The man also said that he would return the kindness and they all departed.

Sometime later the ascetic happened to be passing through the district where the animals lived and decided to visit them. The monkey received him warmly; he went to the mountains and brought to the ascetic all the marvelous fruit growing on the trees. Then the ascetic stopped to see the leopard who was equally amiable in his welcome. But since the leopard had nothing to give to the ascetic, he went to the palace, killed the king's daughter, and took her jewels. He brought these back to the ascetic who had no idea how they had been acquired.

The ascetic took the jewels to the jeweler to sell them. The jeweler recognized them, went to the king, and announced that it was the ascetic who had killed the princess.

They caught the ascetic and paraded him through the city before nailing him on a stake. The snake heard the ascetic's cries and devised a plan to help him. He bit the king's son, who became extremely sick and dreamt that a traveler had been unjustly condemned; he would be cured only if this traveler put his hand on the

The Ascetic Freeing the Jeweler from the Pit
The ascetic, crouched over the pit, is flanked by the monkey, the leopard, and the snake. He throws down a rope to the young man, who sits crosslegged in the pit, which is conceived as a semicircular tunnel enclosed by rocks with a shallow pool of water at the bottom. The bearded ascetic is attired in a blue robe with gold bands and hooded cloak; the clean-shaven jeweler wears a white turban, red robe, and white underpants. The interchange between men and animals is spontaneous; each character communicates freely with the other. The grouping of the figures, with the ascetic and the animals above and the jeweler below, forecasts their future roles: those above will repay the ascetic with kindness, while the one below will cause him harm.

wound. They took the ascetic down from the stake and brought him to the king. The ascetic prayed that the prince be cured, and the king's son miraculously recovered. Then the ascetic told the king how he had saved the animals and the jeweler from the pit and how each had repaid him. The king marveled at his story and gave him many presents. The jeweler was caught, scourged, and executed.

Thus the animals paid what they owed and were freed from their obligations while the man had been ungrateful and false.

History of *Kalila wa Dimna*

The history of the *Kalila wa Dimna* and the transmission of the fables into the Near East can be partially reconstructed from the introductions added to the work in subsequent translations.[1] According to the preface by Ali ibn al-Shah al-Farisi (the Iranian), which appears in some of the Arabic versions, the book was brought to Iran during the reign of Khosrau Nushirvan (531–79), a Sasanian king.[2] The author of this preface is unknown through historical sources and the date the preface was added to the work has not yet been determined.

Ali begins his section by giving an account of the origin of the book, which he traces to the fourth century B.C. After the conquest of India, Alexander the Great (336–23 B.C.) appointed one of his officers to rule that land. Soon after he departed, the people of India deposed the foreign ruler and replaced him with a descendant of one of their own kings, Dabshalim, who proved to be a very cruel and capricious man. A Brahman philosopher named Bidpai tried to teach the king moderation and justice. At first Dabshalim was angry and had Bidpai imprisoned; then he repented, appointed the philosopher his minister, and followed Bidpai's advice on princely behavior. In time his subjects came to adore him and the neighboring princes submitted to his wise rule. The king asked Bidpai to write a book that could be used as a guide to rulers and help them obtain the loyalty of their subjects. The philosopher went into seclusion and within a year composed a book with fourteen chapters, each of which contained a moral question and its answer. He entitled the book *Kalila wa Dimna* and offered it to the king. Bidpai declined the gifts and honors presented to him by Dabshalim and requested only that the book be carefully guarded and preserved.

Bidpai's work became extremely well known, and the news of this marvelous book reached the court of Khosrau Nushirvan. Nushirvan dispatched his physician Burzoe to India with instructions to procure a copy of this book at any cost. Although faced with many obstacles, Burzoe succeeded in obtaining the book and brought it back to Iran, where it was deposited in the royal treasury.

The mission of Burzoe is given in detail in the Arabic translation by Abdallah ibn al-Muqaffa, whose life and works will be discussed later.[3] According to Ibn al-Muqaffa, when Nushirvan heard of the existence of the book, he directed his minister, Buzurjmihr, to find a man with outstanding literary abilities and zeal who was also a scholar well versed in both Sanskrit and Pahlavi. The minister chose Burzoe, a physician, and sent him to India. Burzoe encountered great resistance when he attempted to locate the book. He finally obtained a copy, together with other valuable manuscripts, through an Indian sage who befriended him. The physician worked night and day translating the book into Pahlavi; when he was finished, he departed for Iran.

Burzoe's translation was presented to Nushirvan and read before a large assembly where it won high acclaim. Nushirvan wanted to give the physician expensive gifts to reward his great accomplishment, but Burzoe declined the presents and asked only that a brief account of his life be written and placed at the beginning of the book. This request was granted and Buzurjmihr composed the biography of the physician.[4] It began with Burzoe's early life and traced his first journey to India, where he studied chemistry and medicine and learned Sanskrit. The biography described the mission entrusted to Burzoe by Nushirvan, narrated his second trip to India (when he obtained and translated the *Kalila wa Dimna*), and concluded with praises of Burzoe's achievements and personal qualities. The finished chapter, read before nobles and courtiers of Nushirvan's court, was greatly praised.

These two accounts found in the Arabic translations of the *Kalila wa Dimna* most likely combine fact with fiction. Although the compiler of the Indian fables is not known, he has become identified with the Indian philosopher named Bidpai mentioned by Ali ibn al-Shah. The work appears to have been translated into Pahlavi around 570, presumably by the Iranian physician Burzoe. Almost immediately, the Pahlavi version was translated into Old Syriac, of which an incomplete copy is still in existence. Since both the Sanskrit text and its Pahlavi translation are lost, and the Old Syriac version is unreliable, it is not possible to reconstruct the chapters of the original work and their contents. The Pahlavi version was most likely expanded by additional stories. It has been argued that the Sanskrit *Kalila wa Dimna* contained only five stories from the *Panchatantra;* the Pahlavi version added three stories from the *Mahabharata,* together with four or five tales from other Indian sources. Also added during the Pahlavi translation was the section on Burzoe's mission to India and his biography attributed to Buzurjmihr. Arabic translations embellished the book with extra stories and chapters, such as the prefaces written by Ali ibn al-Shah and Ibn al-Muqaffa, which include a number of parenthetical tales and other fables of local origin.

The *Kalila wa Dimna* as the world knows it is the work of Ibn al-Muqaffa, who translated the book from Pahlavi into Arabic around 750. This rendition includes Burzoe's mission to India and the physician's biography; these sections are followed by Sanskrit fables taken from the *Panchatantra, Mahabharata,* and other Indian classics. Ibn al-Muqaffa wrote an introduction to the book and composed a chapter on Dimna's trial in which the culprit is punished, inserting it after the first story; he also added a tale about an ascetic and his quest.

Ibn al-Muqaffa's version was later expanded by the otherwise unknown Ali ibn Al-Shah, who added a new preface giving an account of the history of the book. In some Arabic copies a story about Burzoe's search for a miraculous plant in India, which leads to his discovery of the *Kalila wa Dimna,* is placed after Ali ibn al-Shah's preface; two short fables are also appended to the end—The Heron and the Duck; and The Dove, the Fox, and the Heron. When these stories were incorporated in Ibn al-Muqaffa's translation is not known and it is difficult to determine their origin, since the book was copied and revised many times in the following years.

The *Kalila wa Dimna* was translated into Syriac, Greek, Ethiopic, Persian, Malay, Hebrew, Spanish, Latin, English, French, German, and Armenian and reworked into Arabic and Persian verse. From the Greek version came other renditions into Latin, Italian, Slovanic, and Croatian; the Hebrew was retranslated into Latin, German, Spanish, Czech, Dutch, Danish, Italian, English, and French.

The Arabic versification was first attempted by a contemporary of Ibn al-Muqaffa, Aban al-Lahiki, whose work is now lost. Another metric version was written around 1100 by Ibn al-Habbariyya; a third was composed in the middle of the thirteenth century.

Ibn al-Muqaffa's *Kalila wa Dimna* was translated into Persian several times. A version, now lost, was rendered into verse by Rudagi (died 916) in the second decade of the tenth century. Firdausi in his introduction to the *Shahnama* mentions that when the Samanid sultan Nasir ibn Ahmad (914–43) heard the story of how the book was brought from India by the physician Burzoe and later translated into Arabic by Ibn al-Muqaffa, he ordered his minister Balami to render the Arabic into Persian.[5] Many persons studied the book, and finally Rudagi composed the Persian versification. This work became so highly regarded that the sultan asked to have it embellished with illustrations.[6]

The next Persian translation was undertaken in the middle of the twelfth century by Nizam al-Din Abu'l-Maali Nasrallah ibn Abd al-Hamid, who dedicated the work to Bahram Shah (1118–52) of Ghazna. A different rendition was transcribed for the Seljuk sultan Izz al-Din Kaikaus II (1246–57) by Ahmad ibn Mahmud al-Tusi in Konya one hundred years later.

Another Persian versification was composed by Husein Vaiz Kashifi (died 1504) in Herat at the court of the Timurid sultan Husein Mirza (1470–1506). Called the *Anvar-i Suheili* (Lights of Canopus) in honor of Ahmad Suheili, the minister of Husein Mirza, this version replaced the chapters written by Burzoe and Ibn al-Muqaffa with a new introduction that offers a different historical setting for the origin of the book.[7] According to Kashifi, the emperor of China was told by his minister the story of the Indian king Dabshalim, who had been directed in a dream to a cave where an old man gave him a treasure. From this treasure Dabshalim kept only the testament of the king of Iran, which contained fourteen rules for princes. He took this to Ceylon, where a Brahman named Bidpai explained each rule by means of a fable, each of which formed a separate chapter in the book.

The *Anvar-i Suheili* was edited in the court of the Mughal emperor Akbar (1556–1605) by his minister Abu'l-Fadl, who completed the work in 1578. Entitled the *Iyar-i Danish* (Touchstone of Knowledge), this version restored the chapters of Burzoe and Ibn al-Muqaffa.

The *Kalila wa Dimna* was translated twice into Eastern Turkish from Nasrallah's Persian, which was also translated into Ottoman Turkish by Masud for Umar Beg (died 1347), the ruler of Aydın in Anatolia. The latter was rendered into verse during the reign of the Ottoman sultan Murad I (1359–89), while another version in prose was produced in the middle of the sixteenth century. The most well-known Turkish translation was made by Ali ibn Salih, who was known as Ali Çelebi. Entitled the *Hümayunname* (Book of Kings), it was dedicated to Sultan Süleyman the Magnificent (1520–66). Ali Çelebi's work was later translated into French, German, Dutch, Hungarian, Swedish, and Malay.

Ibn al-Muqaffa's immensely popular book was also widely imitated. Aside from the tales included in *The Thousand and One Nights,* it inspired the *Sulwan al-Muta* (Prescription for Pleasure) written in 1159 in Sicily by Abdallah ibn Zafar al-Sigilli (the Sicilian). Another rendition was produced around 1000 in the Tabari dialect by Marzuban ibn Rustam, a prince of Tabaristan; entitled the *Marzubannama,* it was recast into classical Persian in the thirteenth century.

Ibn al-Muqaffa's *Kalila wa Dimna* is the earliest extant version of the book and the source for all subsequent translations. Ibn al-Muqaffa, one of the originators of classical Arabic literature, was born around

720 in Fars in southern Iran. He was the son of a tax collector known as al-Muqaffa (the crippled). Called Rozbih at birth, he took the name Abdallah after he embraced Islam. Ibn al-Muqaffa first served the Umayyad governors and officers in Kirman; he then attached himself to the newly-established Abbasids and became secretary to Isa ibn Ali, the uncle of Caliph al-Mansur. He worked in Basra and Kufa, frequenting the society of elite and learned men. Ibn al-Muqaffa was caught in the conflict between the caliph and his rebellious brother and died prematurely around 756, a victim of political intrigue. Asked by his patron to write a letter to the caliph to pardon the rebel, Ibn al-Muqaffa performed this task with such zeal that he aroused the suspicions of al-Mansur, who ordered his death. Ibn al-Muqaffa was last seen entering the house of the governor of Basra, who had been asked by the caliph to dispose of him.

Although Ibn al-Muqaffa died at age thirty-six in the prime of his life, he left a tremendous number of translations and original works.[8] His name is best remembered for the translation of the *Kalila wa Dimna*. There is no reliable and authentic copy of this work, and since the work was copied and revised so many times, the quality of the original prose is virtually lost. His hand is seen in the celebrated biography of Burzoe, which contains criticism of religion and defends reason. He also wrote the chapter on the trial of Dimna, providing a moral conclusion to the story's otherwise cynical ending. It seems clear that the translator was personally involved with the morality presented in the *Kalila wa Dimna* and appended the book to suit his convictions and the prevailing ethics of his age. It is not known whether the other chapters were similarly adjusted, but their strong Hindu flavor suggests that Ibn al-Muqaffa did not alter them significantly.

Ibn al-Muqaffa is recorded as having translated other Pahlavi texts into Arabic, including chronicles of the Sasanians and other historical works of pre-Islamic Iran. Even though most of these texts were lost or reworked by later writers, Ibn al-Muqaffa was singularly influential in reviving ancient Iranian traditions and incorporating them into Arab-Islamic literature. By doing so, he introduced to the Near East the classic Indian fables, which in turn were transmitted to the West and had a universal impact on the genre of parables.

His original works include the *Adab Kabir,* a treatise on advice to princes, and the *Risala fi'l-Sahaba,* an essay reflecting the political, religious, and social problems of his time. Also attributed to him is a text in defense of Manichaeanism, of which he himself was suspected.

Ibn al-Muqaffa was one of the most brilliant exponents of the classical age of Arabic literature; he was a superb linguist and a highly intellectual man who drew upon and exposed to the world the cultural heritage of Iran and India. It is a paradox that his fame has caused much of his own style and writing to suffer, since his works were copied, revised, and translated many times by admirers and imitators.

---

1. The best survey of the work and its translations appears in C. Brockelmann, "Kalila wa-Dimna," *Encyclopedia of Islam,* 2d ed., vol. 4 (Leiden: E. J. Brill; London: Luzac & Co., 1978), pp. 503–6.
2. For the preface by Ali ibn al-Shah see Wyndham Knatchbull, *Kalila and Dimna, or the Fables of Bidpai* (Oxford: W. Baxter, 1819), pp. 1–32; and Ion G. N. Keith-Falconer, *Kalilah and Dimnah, or the Fables of Bidpai* (Amsterdam: Philo Press, 1970), pp. xix–xx.
3. For the mission of Burzoe in Ibn al-Muqaffa's work see Knatchbull, *Kalila and Dimna,* pp. 32–46; and Keith-Falconer, *Kalilah and Dimnah,* pp. xxi–xxii.
4. For the biography of Burzoe according to Ibn al-Muqaffa see Knatchbull, *Kalila and Dimna,* pp. 65–82; and Keith-Falconer, *Kalilah and Dimnah,* pp. xxiv–xxvi.
5. V. Minorsky, "The Older Preface to the *Shah-nama,*" in *Studi Orientalistice in honore di Giorgio Levi della Vida,* vol. 2 (Rome: Istituto per l'Oriente, 1956), pp. 167–68.
6. Ibid., p. 168, note 3. The wording used by Firdausi is ambiguous and is thought to mean that either the Chinese added images to the work or many images were added to it.
7. This work was translated into English in Arthur N. Wollaston, *The Anwar-i Suhaili, or the Lights of Canopus* (London: John Murray, 1904).
8. For Ibn al-Muqaffa's translations and original works see F. Gabrielli, "Ibn al-Mukaffa," *Encyclopedia of Islam,* 2d ed., vol. 3 (1971), pp. 883–85.

Illustrations of *Kalila wa Dimna*

Ibn al-Muqaffa's *Kalila wa Dimna* was not only the most popularly copied and translated book in Islamic literature, but also one that was profusely illustrated. Throughout the Near East Arabic versions as well as Persian and Turkish translations were embellished with paintings.

The earliest reference in the Islamic world to an illustrated version of these fables appears in Tabari's voluminous *Tarikh* (Universal History), written in the first quarter of the tenth century. The author writes that in 841 a Central Asian prince was prosecuted for owning idols and illustrated books; he defended himself by accusing the judge of possessing such a work, a copy of the *Kalila wa Dimna*.[1] Another reference is found in Firdausi's introduction to the *Shahnama*. Firdausi writes that when the work was translated in the tenth century into Persian verse by Rudagi at the court of Nasir ibn Ahmad, many paintings were added to illustrate the text so that "the seeing and the reading of it should please everybody."[2] These illustrations became the most significant feature of the *Kalila wa Dimna*, whose pictorial cycle enchanted generations of readers.

The oldest illustrated manuscript that has surivived is an Arabic version with ninety-eight paintings, now in the Bibliothèque Nationale in Paris.[3] Thought to have been copied in Syria between 1200 and 1220, the work employs simple compositions with a few figures placed either in a landscape suggested by large sprays of plants and flowers or seated under arched and flat-roofed enclosures with minimal furnishings, following the stylistic features of early-thirteenth-century Arabic manuscripts produced in Syria and Iraq. The painter has drawn the elements in free flowing lines and rendered them in pure and bold colors. The illustrations appear to be original and specifically conceived for this manuscript by the anonymous artist, who depicts the animals in naturalistic poses, enacting their given roles with ease and confidence. The paintings in the work, with their charming and spontaneous animal portrayals, became the prototypes for later versions of the *Kalila wa Dimna*. No other illustrated Arabic versions of the *Kalila wa Dimna* have survived from the thirteenth century.[4]

In the fourteenth century the book had an unexplainable revival throughout the Near East, with both Ibn al-Muqaffa's work and its Persian translation by Nasrallah copied and illustrated in Islamic courts.

The earliest illustrated copy of Nasrallah's translation, now in the Topkapı Palace Museum in İstanbul, was produced at the end of the thirteenth century.[5] It contains 124 paintings that reveal the same interest in representing animals in naturalistic poses found in the early-thirteenth-century Arabic manuscript, but the compositions have become more elaborate and the scenes with human figures are considerably more crowded. The overall use of patterns in landscape and architectural settings recalls the style associated with the *Varqa va Gulshah,* executed in Konya in the mid-thirteenth-century,[6] and late-thirteenth- or early-fourteenth-century Iranian paintings assigned to Baghdad and Shiraz. Compositions and figure types also reveal a dependence on manuscript illustrations produced in Syria and Iraq in the first half of the thirteenth century, but they are rendered in a style that appears unique to this manuscript. Whether the work was sponsored in Anatolia or in Iran is still unresolved.

More than a dozen Persian manuscripts, which are either intact or broken up with their paintings pasted into albums, were made in the courts of Tabriz, Baghdad, and Shiraz under the Ilkhanid, Jalairid, Inju, and Muzaffarid sultans who controlled these cities in the fourteenth century. The paintings in these early Persian manuscripts reveal the diverse styles of the studios in which they were produced. Among the Ilkhanid manuscripts is the first dated version of Nasrallah's translation, which was copied in 1307/8. This volume, in the British Library, contains sixty-six illustrations executed in a provincial style.[7] Another work, produced in 1333, reflects the Inju style of Shiraz.[8] Some twenty illustrations of this fragmentary manuscript are presently dispersed among European and American collections.

Some of the paintings from fourteenth-century copies of the *Kalila wa Dimna* were removed from the original volumes and incorporated into imperial albums. A group of seventeen scenes is in one of the albums in the Topkapı Palace Museum,[9] while twenty-five spectacular illustrations were pasted in the so-called Yıldız Album in the collection of the İstanbul University Library.[10] Among the celebrated copies of Nasrallah's translation is the manuscript in Cairo produced for the Ilkhanids in 1343/44 and other late-fourteenth-century works attributed to the Muzaffarid and Jalairid court schools.[11]

The *Kalila wa Dimna* continued to be illustrated in Iran throughout the fifteenth century under the patronage of the Timurid and Turkman princes. The most beautiful paintings were made in Herat for the manuscripts commissioned by the Timurid prince Baysunghur Mirza. One of these works, in the Topkapı Palace Museum, is dated 1429 and contains twenty-six illustrations; a second, also in İstanbul, was completed in 1431 and incorporates nineteen scenes removed from a slightly earlier Turkman manuscript; an exquisite copy in the Gulistan Palace Library in Tehran, once thought to be commissioned by Baysunghur, is now dated circa 1460–65 and attributed to the Turkman court at Baghdad.[12]

The popularity of the *Kalila wa Dimna* in the Timurid capital instigated a new translation, the *Anvar-i Suheili* composed by Kashifi at the end of the fifteenth century. This version had the same success as the work of his predecessor, and many manuscripts based on the revised Persian rendition were illustrated in the following years.[13]

Among the illustrated Persian works is a unique copy of Ahmad ibn Mahmud's translation; this manuscript, executed in 1495 at the Ottoman court in İstanbul, contains seven paintings.[14]

Ali Çelebi's *Hümayunname,* the Turkish translation of Kashifi's work, had a limited appeal and only three (or possibly four) illustrated copies were produced in the second half of the sixteenth century. The earliest of these manuscripts was copied in Cairo in 1567 and contains 30 paintings; another, dated 1589, is more profusely illustrated and possesses 165 scenes; the third, datable to 1595–1600 and assigned to Baghdad, has 87 illustrations.[15] It is interesting to note that the earliest of these Turkish works was executed in Cairo, formerly the capital of the Mamluks, who had sponsored the revival of Ibn al-Muqaffa's book some two hundred years before.

Seven illustrated copies of Ibn al-Muqaffa's *Kalila wa Dimna* are known to have been made in the Mamluk world, either in Egypt or in Syria.[16] Three of these date from the middle of the fourteenth century; the remaining were made either in the second half of the fourteenth century or in the early decades of the fifteenth century. After this period, Arabic versions of the work fell into oblivion and were reproduced sporadically in the ensuing centuries.

The most outstanding Mamluk manuscripts are two versions made in the middle of the fourteenth century: the copy dated 1354, now in the Bodleian Library at Oxford, and an undated volume owned by the Bibliothèque Nationale in Paris.[17] A third work, known only through a single folio found in Cairo, is in the Cambridge University Library.[18] Because of the repetitive nature of the scene depicted—the king of the lions conversing with his mother—it is not possible to assign a specific date to the Cambridge folio. The work was most likely executed in the middle of the fourteenth century, about the same time as the Oxford and Paris manuscripts.

The only one of the four manuscripts produced between the second half of the fourteenth century and early fifteenth century that bears a date is the copy transcribed in 1388 and owned by the Corpus Christi College in Cambridge.[19] A second work, in the Bayerische Staatsbibliothek in Munich, should be dated between the Oxford and Cambridge manuscripts.[20] The others, in Munich and in a private collection, were illustrated after the 1388 copy, possibly in the early fifteenth century.[21]

Only two other illustrated Arabic versions of the *Kalila wa Dimna* are known to have been produced after the Mamluk period. One of these, dated 1672, has more than one hundred scenes that reveal a familiarity with Western painting;[22] another, attributed to the eighteenth century, is pure folk art.[23]

The mid-fourteenth-century copies of the *Kalila wa Dimna* in Oxford and Paris are extremely similar in style. The Oxford volume has seventy-seven paintings and a fragment pasted on the first page. Although the opening folios of the work are missing, the manuscript is intact and contains a colophon, which states that the transcription of the text was completed by Muhammad ibn Ahmad on May 19, 1354. The Paris manuscript was rebound at a later date; several quartos are not in sequence, and its beginning and end are missing. This volume contains fifty paintings of which one is a later addition (fol. 1b), several are fragmentary (fols. 9b, 94a, and 94b), and a number have been "restored" by an incompetent hand.

The paintings in the Paris manuscript are almost identical to those in the Oxford copy, with the exception of two illustrations; one of these represents an episode not found in the Oxford copy—the lion killing the donkey, a parenthetical tale in the chapter on the monkey and the tortoise (fol. 86a)—and an additional scene narrating an episode in the story of the ringdove (fol. 64a). Otherwise, the scenes, including the fragmentary ones, follow the compositional schemes of the Oxford copy. Since the Paris work is incomplete, it is not possible to determine whether the other twenty-seven paintings included in the Oxford copy were part of the original volume. It is also difficult to reconstruct the extent of the narrative cycle and to determine whether the Paris manuscript originally had more paintings than the one in Oxford. Since its colophon is missing, the date it was transcribed is unknown.

Although these two works are basically identical in the treatment of the subject, the Paris manuscript reveals the hand of a more sensitive artist. The drawing of the animals is more spontaneous; compositions flow with greater ease; the ornamental patterns used in landscapes, architecture, and garments have a decorative quality without being schematized. Although it is difficult to differentiate compositions and colors in the two volumes, the painter of the Paris *Kalila wa Dimna* displays a more refined sense of aesthetics and a greater sympathy for his protagonists and is a more competent illustrator than is his colleague who worked on the Oxford copy. Either both men followed a model that is now lost and each executed the paintings to the best of his abilities, or the painter or the Paris manuscript produced the first Mamluk *Kalila wa Dimna* and it was copied almost immediately by the man working on the Oxford copy. It is also possible that the painter of the Oxford copy was the originator and created a more extensive narrative cycle from which the other made a selection of scenes and executed them in his own more refined style.

Both works reveal influences from the earliest Arabic version of the *Kalila wa Dimna,* produced some one hundred and fifty years earlier, as well as the impact of contemporary Mamluk manuscripts devoted to animals. The mid fourteenth century was the golden age of Mamluk art, with members of the court sponsoring a vast number of illuminated manuscripts; brasses inlaid with silver and gold; enameled and gilded glass; luxurious silk textiles; and, above all, spectacular buildings embellished with carved stone and stucco, polychrome marble paneling, and carved wood details.[24] This period also witnessed a renaissance of book painting, with classical Arabic texts—such as the *Maqamat* of al-Hariri and the *Automata* of al-Jazari—copied and illustrated.[25] Among the most popularly illustrated books of the time were texts on botany, zoology, and related sciences, as well as treatises describing the usefulness of animals. The most notable among them was the *Kitab Manafi al-Hayawan* (Book on the Usefulness of Animals) written and transcribed in 1354 by Ibn al-Durayhim al-Mawsili.[26] This work contains ninety-one paintings illustrating domestic and wild animals and birds as well as such creatures as fish, reptiles, worms, and insects. A related work, the *Kitab al-Hayawan* (Book of Animals), written by al-Jahiz in the ninth century and copied by an anonymous scribe in the mid fourteenth century, includes descriptions of animals such as dogs, lions, goats, roosters, elephants, giraffes, crocodiles, and ostriches.[27] The *Kashf al-Asrar* (Disclosure of Secrets) by Ibn Ghanim al-Maqdisi, illustrated in the middle of the fourteenth century, contains representations of animals and birds in addition to flowers.[28] Also illustrated during this period was the *Sulwan al-Muta* (Prescription for Pleasure), a series of fables written by Ibn Zafar al-Sigilli under the influence of Ibn al-Muqaffa.[29]

As observed by the manuscripts discussed above, there was an unprecedented flourish of illustrated books on animals in the Mamluk world in the 1350s. Painters either created scenes for texts that were being illustrated for the first time—such as the *Kitab Manafi al-Hayawan,* the *Kitab al-Hayawan,* and the *Sulwan al-Muta*—or worked on those with a previously established pictorial cycle—such as the *Kalila wa Dimna.*

The patrons of these manuscripts, including the Oxford *Kalila wa Dimna,* are unknown. Only a few illustrated Mamluk manuscripts contain dedicatory pages with names of the patrons. Works that bear dedications indicate that they were sponsored by second-generation mamluks, not by sultans and amirs. The Mamluk court did not commission illustrated literary or scientific texts but concentrated on sponsoring Korans for their religious establishments as well as books on theology, history, geography, and other sciences. Patrons of illustrated manuscripts were generally not identified in historical sources, but their fathers were among the ruling military elite. Included among fourteenth-century patrons are Nasir al-Din Muhammad, son of an official named Husam al-Din Taranbay, who commissioned the *Maqamat* dated 1337 in the Bodleian Library.[30] Another Nasir al-Din Muhammad ordered in 1354 the *Automata* now in İstanbul;[31] he was the son of Tulaq al-Hasani al-Maliki al-Salihi, who served both Sultan Hasan and Sultan Salih and became the chief military judge of Damascus in 1350. A copy of the *Kashf al-Gunum,* a text on musical instruments in the Topkapı Palace Museum,[32] was produced in the mid fourteenth century for Sayf al-Din Abu Bakr, son of an otherwise unknown amir named Minglibugha.

Names of fourteenth-century Mamluk calligraphers and painters also are rarely provided in the colophons of illustrated manuscripts. Known copyists included Farrukh ibn Abd al-Latif, who completed in 1315 the *Automata* that was formerly in İstanbul;[33] Abu'l-Fadail ibn Abu Ishaq was the calligrapher of the 1354 *Maqamat* now in Vienna;[34] Ibn al-Durayhim al-Mawsili transcribed in 1354 his own work entitled *Kitab Manafi al-Hayawan;*[35] Muhammad ibn Ahmad al-Izmiri copied the 1354 *Automata* in Vienna; Umar ibn Abdallah ibn Umar al-Shafii copied in 1366 the *Nihayat al-Su'l wa'l-Umniyya,* a book on horsemanship now in Dublin;[36] the latter work was transcribed in 1371 by Ahmad ibn Umar;[37] and a third version was completed in 1373 by Ahmad al-Misri.[38]

A painter named Ghazi ibn Abd al-Rahman al-Dimashqi illustrated around the year 1300 a copy of the *Maqamat;*[39] and Ali painted the scenes in the *Nihayat al-Su'l wa'l-Umniyya* of 1366 mentioned earlier.

Muhammad ibn Ahmad, the calligrapher of the Oxford *Kalila wa Dimna,* did not sign any other works and is known only by this singular manuscript. The painter of the work remains anonymous.

Following the style of the age, the artist who executed the paintings in the Oxford *Kalila wa Dimna* employed the decorative themes and figure types found in mid-fourteenth-century Mamluk book illustration. The compositions, placement of figures within architectural settings, and landscape elements owe much to the first illustrated Arabic version of the text, produced more than one hundred years earlier. Similar to the older manuscript, the illustrations in the Oxford volume were intended to embellish the book and portray the characters involved in the stories. Stressing simplicity and clarity, they represent only essential elements. Heroes and heroines perform their roles in pairs or in groups, placed against settings that contain only minimal props. This practice of eliminating extraneous details accentuates the figures and their actions, forcing the viewer to concentrate on the narrative, which is the primary concern of the illustrator.

---

1. See Jill S. Cowen, "The Istanbul University Kalila wa Dimna: An Il-Khanid Masterpiece," Ph.D. dissertation, New York University, Institute of Fine Arts, 1980, p. 44; Emel Esin, "Basil Gray: *La Peinture Persane.*" Review article. *Belleten* 26 (1962): 378.
2. V. Minorsky, "The Older Preface to the Shah-nama," in *Studi Orientalistice in honore di Giorgio Levi della Vida,* vol. 2 (Rome: Istituto per l'Oriente, 1956), p. 168.
3. Arabe 3465. Kurt Holter, "Die islamischen Miniaturhandschriften vor 1350," *Zentralblatt für Bibliothekwesen* 54 (1937): 1–37, no. 26; Hugo Buchthal, Otto Kurz, and Richard Ettinghausen, "Supplementary Notes to K. Holter's Check List of Islamic Illuminated Manuscripts Before A.D. 1350," *Ars Islamica* 7 (1940): 147–64, no. 26; Richard Ettinghausen, *Arab Painting* (Geneva: Albert Skira, 1962), pp. 62–63. See also Hugo Buchthal, "Hellenistic Miniatures in Early Islamic Manuscripts," *Ars Islamica* 7 (1940): 125–33, figs. 23, 25, 27–28, 30–31, 33–36, 38–39, 41–42, 44, and 46; and idem., "Indian Fables in Islamic Art," *Journal of the Royal Asiatic Society* (1941): 317–24, figs. 1, 3, and 7; Cowen, "Istanbul University," pp. 46–51 and 72–74.
4. There is, however, a singular copy of Sad al-Din al-Varavini's Persian work called the *Marzubannama* illustrated in 1299 in Baghdad. This work, in İstanbul, Archaeological Museum Library, 216, has only three figural compositions in the introduction. Marianna S. Simpson, "The Role of Baghdad in the Formation of Persian Painting," *Le Monde Iranien et Islam,* in press.
5. H. 363. M. Ş. İpsiroğlu, *Das Bild im Islam* (Vienna and Munich: Verlag Anton Schroll & Co., 1971), pls. 7–14; Filiz Çağman and Zeren Tanındı, *Topkapı Saray Museum: Islamic Miniature Painting* (İstanbul: Güzel Sanatlar Matbaası, 1979), no. 7; Cowen, "Istanbul University," pp. 52–59 and 74–75.
6. İstanbul, Topkapı Palace Museum, H. 841. Assadullah Souren Melekian-Chirvani, "Le Roman de Varqe et Golšâh," *Ars Asiatiques* 22 (1970); Çağman and Tanındı, *Topkapı Saray Museum,* no. 6.
7. Or. 13506. P. Waley and Norah M. Titley, "An Illustrated Persian Text of Kalila and Dimna Dated 707/1307–8,"

British Library Journal 1, no. 1 (1975): 42–61; Cowen, "'Istanbul University," pp. 66–68 and 76.

8. Ernst J. Grube, *Muslim Miniature Paintings from the XIII to XIX Century from Collections in the United States and Canada* (Venice: Neri Pozza, 1962), pp. 36–39 and nos. 28–29; Cowen, "Istanbul University," pp. 68–70 and 77–78.
9. H. 2152, fol. 60a. F. Sarre and F. R. Martin, *Die Ausstellung von Meisterwerken Muhammedanischer Kunst in München 1910* (Munich: Bei F. Bruckmann, 1912), vol. 1, pl. 6; Cowen, "Istanbul University," pp. 59–66 and 75.
10. F. 1422. These paintings, their style, and provenance are thoroughly discussed in Cowen, "Istanbul University."
11. National Library, 61. Ernst Kühnel, "A Bidpai Manuscript of 1343/4 (744 H.) in Cairo," *Bulletin of the American Institute for Iranian Art and Archaeology* 5 (1937): 137–41. For this work and other illustrated Persian manuscripts see also Basil Gray, "Fourteenth-Century Illustrations of the *Kalilah* and *Dimnah*," *Ars Islamica* 7 (1940): 134–40; and Ivan Stchoukine, *La peinture des manuscrits timurids* (Paris: Paul Geuther, 1954), no. V and pls. II–III.
12. For the manuscripts in Tehran, Gulistan Palace Library, and İstanbul, Topkapı Palace Museum (R. 1022, dated 1429, and H. 362, dated 1431), see Stchoukine, *La peinture des manuscrits timurids,* nos. XXXV–XXXVI; B. W. Robinson, "The Tehran Manuscript of Kalila wa Dimna: A Reconsideration," *Oriental Art* 4 (1958): 108–15; Basil Gray, *Persian Painting* (Geneva: Albert Skira, 1961), pp. 82–84 and title page; B. W. Robinson, "Prince Baysunghur and the Fables of Bidpai," *Oriental Art* 16 (1970): 145–54; Ernst J. Grube and Eleanor Sims, "The School of Herat from 1400 to 1450," in *The Arts of the Book in Central Asia: 14th–16th Centuries,* edited by Basil Gray (Paris: Serinda Publications/UNESCO, 1979), pp. 147–78, figs. 91–93 and pls. XLVII–XLIX. Ernst J. Grube, "Two Kalilah wa Dimnah Codices Made for Baysunghur Mirza: The Concept of the 'Classical Style' Reconsidered," in *Atti del III Convegno Internazionale sull'Arte e sulla Civiltà Islamica: "Problemi dell'età timuride"* (Venice: University of Venice, 1980), pp. 115–22, plus appendix. Other fifteenth-century illustrated copies of the *Kalila wa Dimna* are discussed in Stchoukine, *La peinture des manuscrits timurids,* nos. XI and XLIX.
13. The earliest of these, dated 1502, is in London, British Library, Or. 2799. Norah M. Titley, *Miniatures from Persian Manuscripts, Catalogue and Subject Index of Paintings from Persia, India and Turkey in the British Library and the British Museum* (London: British Library, 1977), no. 189. For other sixteenth- and seventeenth-century copies of this work see ibid., nos. 188 and 190–92; B. W. Robinson, *A Descriptive Catalogue of the Persian Paintings in the Bodleian Library* (Oxford: Clarendon Press, 1958), pp. 87 and 171; idem., *Persian Painting in the John Rylands Library* (London: Sotheby Parke Bernet, 1980), nos. 687–90; Ivan Stchoukine, *Les peintures des manuscrits safavids* (Paris: Paul Geuthner, 1959), nos. 185 and 199. One of the most elaborate copies was produced in the Mughal court in early seventeenth century. Titley, *Miniatures from Persian Manuscripts,* no. 188. Also illustrated in India in the late sixteenth or early seventeenth century was a copy of the *Iyar-i Danish,* the Persian translation by Abu'l-Fadl. This manuscript, in Dublin, Chester Beatty Library, originally had 164 paintings, of which 96 have survived. Thomas W. Arnold and J. V. S. Wilkinson, *The Library of A. Chester Beatty: A Catalogue of the Indian Miniatures* (London: Emery Walker Ltd., 1936), no. 4, pls. 38–47. It did not, however, have the same popularity as the earlier Persian versions, and only two or three illustrated copies were produced in the following centuries.
14. Bombay, Prince of Wales Museum, 51.34. Glynn M. Meredith-Owens, "A Persian Manuscript of the Reign of Bāyezīd II with Ottoman Miniatures," *Bulletin of the Prince of Wales Museum in Western India* 10 (1967): 27–31.
15. The manuscript dated 1567 is in İstanbul, Topkapı Palace Museum, H. 359. Güner İnal, "Kahire'de Yapılmış bir Hümâyünnâme'nin Minyatürleri," *Belleten* 40 (1976): 439–65. The second, dated 1589, is in London, British Library, Add. 15153. Glynn M. Meredith-Owens, *Turkish Miniatures* (London, British Museum, 1963), pp. 27–28, pls. V–VI, XIII–XIV, and XVIII–XX. The undated work is also in the Topkapı Palace Museum, R. 843. Çağman and Tanındı, *Topkapı Saray Museum,* no. 169. Five folios in Boston, Museum of Fine Arts, 14.554–58, appear to belong to a fourth manuscript. Ananda Coomaraswamy, "Miniatures from Turkish and Persian Book of Fables," *Bulletin of the Boston Museum of Fine Arts* 26 (1928): 89–91; idem., *Les Miniatures orientales de la collection Goloubew au Museum of Fine Arts de Boston* in *Ars Asiatica,* vol. 13 (Paris and Brussels: G. van Oest, 1929), p. 65 and pl. LXIV:103a–e.
16. Four of these manuscripts, in Mu-

nich, Oxford, Paris, and Cambridge, are discussed in Sofie Walzer, "The Mamluk Illuminated Manuscripts of Kalila wa-Dimna," in *Aus der Welt der Islamischen Kunst, Festschrift für Ernst Kühnel,* edited by Richard Ettinghausen (Berlin: Verlag Gebr. Mann, 1959), pp. 195–206.

17. Arabe 3467. Ettinghausen, *Arab Painting,* p. 155; Duncan Haldane, *Mamluk Painting* (Warminster, England: Aris & Phillips, Ltd., 1978), pp. 95–99. See also Walzer, "Mamluk Illuminated Manuscripts."
18. FS Box Ar. 51, fol. 60. Sofie Walzer, "An Illustrated Leaf from a Lost Mamluk Kalilah wa-Dimnah Manuscript," *Ars Orientalis* 2 (1957): 503–5.
19. MS 574. This manuscript is written on parchment and has 120 paintings. Haldane, *Mamluk Painting,* pp. 44–46.
20. Cod. Arab 616. Haldane, *Mamluk Painting,* pp. 81–82.
21. Cod. Arab 615. Holter, "Die Islamischen Miniaturhandschriften," no. 79.
22. Manchester, John Rylands University Library, Arabe 487. David James, "Arab Painting," *Marg* 29, no. 3 (June 1976): fig. 35.
23. İstanbul, Archaeological Museum Library, 344. Ettinghausen, *Arab Painting,* p. 81.
24. Esin Atıl, *Renaissance of Islam: Art of the Mamluks* (Washington, D.C.: Smithsonian Institution Press, 1981).
25. For surveys of Mamluk painting see ibid., pp. 250–65; Ettinghausen, *Arab Painting,* pp. 143–60; and Haldane, *Mamluk Painting.*
26. Madrid, Escorial Library, Arabe 898. Eustache de Lorey, "Le Bestiaire de l'Escorial," *Gazette des Beaux-Arts* 14 (1935): 228–38; Ettinghausen, *Arab Painting,* p. 3; James, "Arab Painting," fig. 23; Haldane, *Mamluk Painting,* pp. 50–51.
27. Milan, Bibliotheca Ambrosiana, S. P. 67. Oscar Löfgren and Carl Johan Lamm, *Ambrosian Fragments of an Illuminated Manuscript Containing the Zoology of al-Ǧahiz* (Uppsala, Sweden: Lundequistska Bokhandeln, 1946). A work with the same title, written in Persian by Ibn Bakhtishu, was illustrated in the Ilkhanid court at Maragha in Iran. This manuscript, now in New York, Pierpont Morgan Library, M 500, was heavily repainted during the Safavid period.
28. İstanbul, Süleymaniye Library, Lala İsmail, 565. Ettinghausen, *Arab Painting,* pp. 159–60; Haldane, *Mamluk Painting,* pp. 52–53.
29. This manuscript is now in a private collection in Kuwait. Haldane, *Mamluk Painting,* pp. 59–60. See also *Art Musulman,* sale catalogue by René and Claude Boisgirard, March 24, 1975 (Paris: Hotel George V, 1975), no. 131. Two folios are in Washington, D.C., Freer Gallery of Art. Esin Atıl, *Art of the Arab World* (Washington, D.C.: Freer Gallery of Art, 1975), nos. 53–54. A third folio is in Geneva, Sadruddin Aga Khan Collection. Anthony Welch, *Collection of Islamic Art: Prince Sadruddin Aga Khan* (Geneva: Château de Bellerive, 1978), A. M. 4. An interesting illustrated version, produced in Morocco in the sixteenth century, reveals a strong Western influence. This manuscript, in Madrid, Escorial Library, Arabe 528, is published in Rachel Arié, *Miniatures hispano-musulmanes: Recherches sur un manuscrit arabe illustré de l'Escurial* (Leiden: E. J. Brill, 1969); James, "Arab Painting," fig. 31.
30. Marsh 458. Ettinghausen, *Arab Painting,* p. 152; James, "Arab Painting," fig. 22; Haldane, *Mamluk Painting,* pp. 83–84.
31. The original manuscript, in İstanbul Süleymaniye Library, Aya Sofya, 3606, now has fourteen illustrations. At least twenty-two other paintings have been removed and are now in various private and public collections. Atıl, *Art of the Arab World,* no. 52; Haldane, *Mamluk Painting,* p. 55.
32. A. 3465. Fehmi E. Karatay, *Topkapı Sarayı Müzesi Kütüphanesi: Arapca Yazmalar Kataloğu* (İstanbul: Topkapı Sarayı Müzesi, 1962–69), no. 7424.
33. For a full bibliography of this work see Atıl, *Renaissance of Islam,* no. I.
34. Ibid., no. II. See also Kurt Holter, "Die Galen-Handschrift und die Makamen des Harîrî der Wiener Nationalbibliothek," *Jahrbuch der Kunsthistorischen Sammlungen in Wien* n.s. 9, special no. 104 (1937): 15–35; and Haldane, *Mamluk Painting,* pp. 100–103.
35. See note 26.
36. The Chester Beatty Library, Add. Cat. MS 1. David James, "Mamluke Painting at the Time of the 'Lusignan Crusade,' 1365–90: A Study of the Chester Beatty *Nihayat al-su'l wa'l-umniya . . .* manuscript of 1366," *Humaniora Islamica* 2 (1974): 73–87; Atıl, *Renaissance of Islam,* no. IV.
37. London, British Library, Add. 18866. Rex. G. Smith, *Medieval Muslim Horsemanship: A Fourteenth-Century Arabic Cavalry Manual* (London: British Library, 1979).
38. İstanbul, Topkapı Palace Museum, A. 2651. James, "Mamluke Painting," figs. 3 and 8; Haldane, *Mamluk Painting,* p. 58. A copy of the same work, transcribed in 1383 by Ali ibn Hamid, has blank spaces for illustrations. London, British Library, Add. 23487. James, "Mamluke Painting," p. 74.
39. London, British Library, Or. 9718. Haldane, *Mamluk Painting,* pp. 62–63; L. A. Mayer, "A Hitherto Unknown Damascene Artist," *Ars Islamica* 9 (1942): 168.

The Bodleian Library Manuscript

The Bodleian Library *Kalila wa Dimna* transcribed by Muhammad ibn Ahmad in 1354 (Pococke 400) is the earliest dated copy of this work produced in the Mamluk period. It is a fairly large manuscript, measuring 36.5 centimeters (14⅜ inches) high and 25.0 centimeters (9⅞ inches) wide. The volume contains 162 folios of which 5 at the beginning and 5 at the end are blank and were added during a later restoration.

The original manuscript, which according to the pagination, begins on folio 6a, consists of 147 folios with 77 illustrations, excluding the fragmentary painting with text pasted on folio 5b. The work contains an Ottoman binding datable to the seventeenth century, which suggests either that the manuscript was repaired in the seventeenth century or the Ottoman binding was reused when the volume was restored at a later date. This binding has a dark brown leather ground; the central medallion with pendants on its vertical axis and the four quadrants are rendered in dark red leather, stamped with floral designs and accentuated by gold lines. The doublures with marbled paper, as well as the brown leather flap and spine, are later additions and appear to have been made during a subsequent restoration. Also dating from this period of restoration are new margins placed around the folios and strips of paper pasted over some of the paintings in an unfortunate attempt at preservation.

Fifteen lines of text written in naskhi script appear on each folio and are enclosed by a thin red border. The paintings placed within the text, are generally devoid of frames and transgress into the margins. They often occupy two-thirds of the folios, with identifications of the subjects written in red or black ink above each scene.

Even though the text begins on folio 6a, only one or two sheets appear to be missing from the work: the opening page with an illuminated heading, possibly containing a dedication; and the description of the work, together with the beginning of the table of contents with the title and summary of the first chapter. This copy alters the sequence of the chapters normally found in other Arabic versions of the *Kalila wa Dimna:* the preface of Ali ibn al-Shah is not included and the table of contents, usually found at the end of Ibn al-Muqaffa's introduction, has been moved to the beginning of the volume; the mission of Burzoe, which often follows Ali's preface, is placed after the table of contents without a separate heading. According to the table of contents, the first chapter is the introduction by Ibn al-Muqaffa; it is followed by the biography of Burzoe; chapters three through fifteen contain thirteen fables. Chapter seven combines two short stories—The Monkey and the Tortoise and The Ascetic and the Weasel. The sequence of some of the fables is rearranged; for instance, the story of The Wise Bilar and Queen Ilar is placed after chapter seven rather than near the end of the book. Three fables, thought to be later additions to the *Kalila wa Dimna*—The King of the Mice; The Heron and the Duck; and The Dove, the Fox, and the Heron—are omitted.

The colophon, which appears on the last page (fol. 152b), has only eleven lines of text; the rest of the folio was pasted over with a strip of paper during the restoration. Fortunately, the portion of the text left untouched includes the date and the name of the calligrapher: the work was completed on Monday, the twenty-fifth day of Rabii II, in the year 755 of Hijra (May 19, 1354), by Muhammad ibn Ahmad ibn Safi ibn Qasim ibn Abd al-Rahman al-Sufi, known as Ibn al-Ghazuli. There is no mention of where the work was copied, and the name of the patron is not provided. Muhammad ibn Ahmad does not indicate whether he only transcribed the work or was also responsible for the illustrations.

The *Kalila wa Dimna* was acquired in Syria by Edward Pococke (1604–91), who collected Islamic manuscripts while he was chaplain to the English merchants at Aleppo from 1630 to 1635. Upon returning to England, Pococke was appointed the first Laudian Professor of Arabic at the University of Oxford, and the *Kalila wa Dimna* was purchased together with his other manuscripts by the Bodleian Library in 1692.

The work was most likely produced in Syria and kept there until it was acquired by Pococke in the early 1630s. The manuscript, which may have contained the Ottoman binding at that time, underwent a major restoration after it entered the Bodleian Library.

The Setting and Cast of Characters

Excluding the fragment pasted in the beginning of the book (fig. 1), thirty-three paintings depict only human figures, each supplied with a golden halo; thirty-three others represent animals; and eleven include both men and animals. Twenty scenes with men and women take place indoors; three are devoid of any specific setting, with the figures placed on a ground line formed by a strip of rug (figs. 5, 70, and 74). Seventeen scenes, including two with animals, are framed by an arch (figs. 4, 8, 12–15, 22, 40, 49, 56, 58, and 61); at times a smaller archway is added to the side (figs. 9–11) or two columns divide the arch into a tripartite unit (figs. 51 and 55).

Twenty-four scenes with human figures, including those with animals, take place outdoors, with the ground line formed by a strip of overlapping green leaves or blades of grass (figs. 2–3, 7, 16, 21, 23, 26, 29, 33, 37–38, 42, 57, 62, 64–67, 72–73, and 75). In two of the outdoor scenes, a rug replaces grass as the ground line (figs. 6 and 60); in another it is represented by water (fig. 71). Human figures are generally portrayed in pairs (fifteen scenes); they also appear in groups of threes (ten scenes) or fours (six scenes); rarely are the figures alone or in groups of five.

The furnishings of the interior scenes are extremely simple. Figures generally sit on a carpeted floor under an archway with decorated spandrels; at times circular or triangular projections indicating a roof are added to the center of the arch. Bowls with fruit or flowers are suspended over the figures (figs. 4–5, 8–9, 12–13, 15, 22, 55, and 70); sometimes these bowls are substituted by lamps or flanked by lighting fixtures (figs. 11 and 22). In scenes representing the ruler, the king sits on a high throne, while other figures either stand or, as in the case of the philosopher, sit on the floor. Episodes taking place in bedrooms show a couple in bed, which may be a platform with four legs (fig. 9, 22, and 49) or a mattress placed on the floor (figs. 12–13). The time of day is indicated by candles burning in lamps; in one scene night is symbolized by a deep blue sky, in the center of which is a golden moon with a human face (fig. 13). Also included are props necessitated by the stories, such as baskets (figs. 9–10), jars and bowls (figs. 40, 55, and 58), equipment for metalworking together with a bracelet and cymbals (fig. 15), a crib with an infant (fig. 56), and oblong cushions (figs. 4, 40, 51, 55, 67, 70, and 74).

Landscape elements in scenes with humans are as abbreviated as the interior furnishings, consisting of trees with one or two branches bearing large leaves and buds that recall lotus blossoms. In a unique scene, which depicts a figure emerging from a tree (fig. 33), the tree is large and densely foliated. As specified by the text, rocks, ponds, and wells are incorporated into the landscape (figs. 7, 16, 26, 42, and 71), as well as baskets (figs. 7 and 37) and stakes (figs. 62 and 72). One scene represents a dais or platform for a speaker (fig. 6).

The majority of interior and exterior scenes represent the king seated on his throne, conversing with the philosopher (figs. 2, 5, 60, 64, 67, 70, and 74). In one instance he is accompanied by a swordbearer (fig. 5) and elsewhere with additional courtiers (fig. 2). The king is also shown riding an elephant (fig. 75) and participating in one of the stories (figs. 57–58 and 61). The prince, a beardless version of the king, appears in two scenes illustrating the tale of the fantastic bird (figs. 65–66).

The king, almost always with a black beard and mustache (except in figs. 5 and 57), is crowned and wears a robe with a floral, geometric, or moiré pattern with gold bands decorating the neck, cuffs, hem, and armbands. He sits crosslegged on a throne with a high back covered with fabric employing floral or geometric designs (in fig. 5 the textile has flying birds). A semicircular fabric is draped over the seat of the throne, which rests on four legs. His garment has either a round neck with a frontal slit or crosses over from right to left. In one scene he holds a sword (fig. 2). The prince is dressed in identical garments.

The next most frequently encountered human type is the ascetic, who appears in ten paintings (figs. 21–23, 40, 51, 55–57, 71, and 73). He plays an important role in the fables, symbolizing the wise person whose lifestyle and actions are models for other humans. He is bearded and attired in a hooded cloak with a moiré design; the cloak opens at times to expose a robe with floral or moiré patterns. A related figure is the Indian sage who is also bearded but dark skinned; he wears a loincloth with a cape and gold armlets and bracelets (fig. 4). Another important personage is the *qadi* or judicial officer, whose only distinction is that he has a white turban, the ends of which either flow down or drape around the chin (figs. 23 and 33).

Male figures, who appear in thirty-three scenes as well as in eleven paintings with animals, are depicted as middle-aged persons with black beards, white turbans, and robes similar to those worn by kings and princes. In one case the turban is green (fig. 2), a color used by the *sayyids* (those who can trace their lineage to the Prophet Muhammad); in another scene the turban is mauve (fig. 6).

Bearded men are usually accompanied by beardless figures (in twenty-four scenes) who are similarly attired. These figures generally represent young courtiers (figs. 2, 5, and 75), adolescents (fig. 51), lovers (fig. 14), workers (figs. 7 and 10), as well as thieves and other criminals (figs. 9, 12–13, 62, and 71–72). Burzoe is also portrayed as a beardless figure in one scene (fig. 4) and possibly in two others as well (figs. 3 and 6). Two paintings depict a man wearing a tall pointed cap (figs. 73 and 75); two others represent a man attired in a short skirt or loincloth (figs. 7 and 16). One unique painting shows a baby in a crib (fig. 56), while another portrays an old man with a white beard (fig. 33). A few men (Burzoe and attendants, the *qadi,* the ascetic, and the king) are shown riding horses, donkeys, or elephants (figs. 3, 33, 73, and 75). An execution by nailing on a stake occurs in two paintings (figs. 62 and 72) and involves partially clothed criminals.

Female figures, who play significant roles in the fables, appear in ten scenes, always in the company of men (figs. 12–14, 22–23, 37–38, 49, 58, and 61). In one scene a woman wears a cap with a front section extending to the crown in a T formation (fig. 14); in two others she is crowned and portrays Queen Ilar (figs. 58 and 61). In these paintings women wear a short-sleeved coat over a robe. Two other scenes depict women wearing shawls over their heads (figs. 23 and 38). Four scenes take place in a bedroom with couples in bed; one of these shows the pair dressed (fig. 13), while in the others they lie naked under the covers (figs. 12, 22, and 49). A singular scene represents two topless women; they are attired only in short skirts and their heads are covered with scarves tied at the temples with a ribbon (fig. 37); the same headdress appears on the owner of the brothel (fig. 22).

Animals, who figure in thirty-three scenes and in the company of men in eleven other paintings, are more colorful and varied than their human counterparts. The lion, the king of the animal kingdom, is portrayed in eleven scenes; the jackal appears in nine; the crow in eight; the mouse and tortoise in six; the hare and monkey in five; the owl in four; the wolf, dove, and snake in three; the fox, gazelle, ox, leopard, and elephant in two; while the cat, camel, goat, weasel, partridge, heron, geese, falcon, crab, and fish make single appearances. Also represented is a fantastic talking bird (figs. 65–66) and a dragon (fig. 16).

Animals appear in outdoor settings identical to those observed in scenes representing humans. Props essential to the stories include a drum hanging from a densely foliated tree (fig. 19), sky with a moon (fig. 47), cage (fig. 35), nest filled with grain (fig. 59), skinned cubs (fig. 76), as well as nets (figs. 39 and 63), sticks (figs. 29 and 42), and flames (figs. 32 and 50). Also depicted are rocks with stylized patterns and bold colors, on top of which the characters stand to address their friends and subjects (figs. 44–46 and 48). These rocks at times flank pools that reflect images (figs. 16, 25, and 47) or become caves in which creatures dwell (figs. 39, 41, and 63) and in which enemies are burned (fig. 50). One rare scene represents a rocky terrain over which birds fly (fig. 43). Ponds required in several stories are framed by the same overlapping green leaves that form the ground line, with the blue water painted in stylized patterns (figs. 26, 41, and 52–54). In one painting the water is reddish and unframed, possibly depicting a shallow marsh (fig. 24).

With the exception of three paintings that represent a single figure (figs. 19 and 76–77), one half of the scenes with animals show them in pairs, while the other half portrays them in groups. Scenes with two protagonists depict animals conversing (figs. 17, 31, 34–35, 52–54, and 68), fighting (figs. 24, 27, 30, and 59), or enacting specific episodes (figs. 25, 47, and 78). Groups are also included in conversation scenes in which the speaker is placed at one side and addresses an audience ranging from two to five members (figs. 18, 20, 36, 44–46, 48, and 69). These groups either represent the same species—such as crows and hares—or have mixed participants—including the jackal, wolf, ox, leopard, owl, and crow. The same heterogeneous combination of characters appears in action scenes in which the protagonists wage war (figs. 43 and 50), kill their prey (fig. 28), or enact one of the scenes (figs. 32, 39, 41, and 63). Animals are represented in characteristic poses, whether conversing or actively taking part in the stories. Their body movements are natural, faces expressive, and interaction realistic.

The lion is painted sandy yellow with a flowing mane (figs. 18, 20, 25, 27–28, 30, 34, 68–69, and 76–77). The jackal Dimna is brownish orange with a golden neck (figs. 17–18, 20, 31, and 35–36); his brother Kalila also has a golden neck but his coat is mauve (figs. 17, 31, and 35). Kalila's coloring appears on other jackals (figs. 28, 36, and 68–69). The mouse, seen in three scenes in the company of men, is charcoal gray (figs. 39–42 and 63), except when specified by the text as being black or white (fig. 16). The hare is pinkish mauve (figs. 25, 36, and 45–47); one individual is colored brownish orange as is Dimna (fig. 46). The monkey, shown in one scene with men, is a gray creature wearing a wide gold collar or necklace (figs. 32, 52–54, and 71). The wolf, painted brownish orange as well as mauve, recalls both the jackals and the fox (figs. 28, 36, and 69). The fox, who is distinguished by his long bushy tail, is joined by men in a single scene; he is brownish orange with a golden neck and resembles Dimna (figs. 19 and 21). The pinkish mauve gazelle with two black horns has a golden neck (figs. 41–42). The ox is white with large black spots; he has brown horns and wears a gold necklace (figs. 20 and 30). The leopard is white with small black spots and has a golden neck (figs. 36 and 71). The large gray elephant with long white tusks (figs. 27 and 47), also seen as the mount of the king when he is bedecked with anklets, necklace, and other trinkets (fig. 75), wears a scalloped gold cap.

Animals appearing in single scenes include a mauve camel with a gold necklace (fig. 28), a weasel who resembles the mouse but has a lighter gray coat (fig. 63), a cat whose coloring is the same as the ox, except that he has a golden neck (fig. 63), and a pair of mauve goats with enormous orange horns and gold collars (fig. 21).

The creatures who inhabit the skies are equally colorful. The crow is dark gray with golden shoulders and black feathers accentuating his head, tips of his tail, and wings (figs. 28, 39, 41, 43–44, and 50); in three scenes he is shown with a golden neck instead of golden shoulders (figs. 44, 48, and 78). The owls are orange with huge golden eyes (figs. 43, 48, 50, and 63). In contrast to all other animals, the king of the owls bears a halo in one scene (fig. 48). Other birds include doves with light and dark blue feathers and golden shoulders (figs. 32, 39, and 59); an orange partridge with mauve wings, blue eyes and beak, and gold necklace (fig. 78); a heron, falcon, and two geese with the same coloring as the doves (figs. 24, 29, and 38); and a talking bird with magnificent blue, red, mauve, and golden plumes (figs. 65–66).

The most frequently represented animal among the creatures who live in water is the tortoise, whose body is mauve, his shell either brown and tan (figs. 41 and 52–54), orange and golden (fig. 29), or pink (fig. 42). The snake, found in three scenes with men, is dark gray (figs. 51 and 71), except when specified by the text as being either black or white (fig. 16). Other sea animals include the mauve and gold crab (fig. 24) and the silver blue fish (fig. 26). The unique dragon, lurking at the bottom of a well, has mauve scales and wears a gold necklace (fig. 16).

Fig. 1. Fragment with Tree (fol. 5b)

The Stories

To avoid confusion, the existing pagination of the manuscript will be used in the description of the chapters and their illustrations. As mentioned earlier, although the text begins on folio 6a, only one or two pages appear to be missing from the beginning of the book. The fragment of a painting (fig. 1) pasted on folio 5b represents a tree with a piece of wood and a saw; it may have belonged to the tale of the monkey and the carpenter, one of the first parenthetical stories in chapter three. If this fragment was part of the Bodleian manuscript, then it would have been placed between folio 40b, Kalila and Dimna Conversing, and folio 41b, Dimna with Two Lions.

Contents
Fols. 6a–8a

The first line in this section belongs to the description of chapter one, the beginning of which is missing. The following folios contain the titles of the stories in the remaining fourteen chapters and give a summary of the moral lessons.

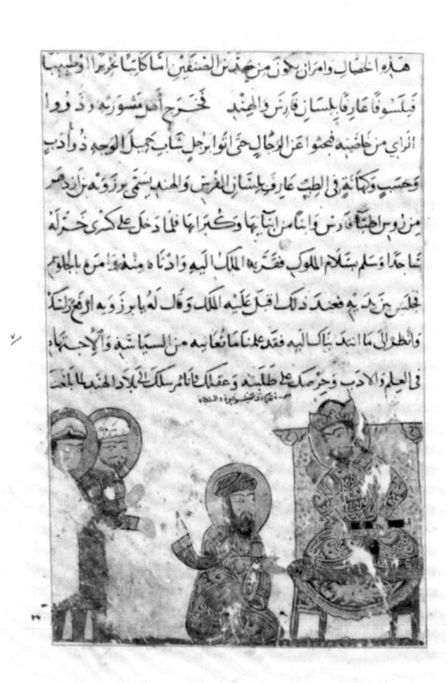

Fig. 2. Burzoe Brought before Nushirvan (fol. 10a)

Fig. 4. Burzoe with the Indian Sage (fol. 13b); *color illustration, page 14*

Preface **The Mission of Burzoe**
Fols. 8b–19a; figs. 2–6

Nushirvan, the king of Iran, hears of the existence of a marvelous book in India and instructs his minister, Buzurjmihr, to find a man with linguistic abilities and a passion for learning to procure the book for him. The minister chooses for this mission Burzoe, a learned physician, who is approved by the king and dispatched to India. Burzoe succeeds in obtaining the book from an Indian sage and translates it into Pahlavi. Upon returning to the court of Nushirvan, Burzoe refuses the gifts bestowed upon him by the king and asks only that his biography be composed by Buzurjmihr and placed at the beginning of the volume.

Fig. 3. Burzoe Traveling to India (fol. 12b); *color illustration, page 13*

Fig. 5. Burzoe Received by Nushirvan (fol. 16a)

Fig. 6. Buzurjmihr Reciting the Biography of Burzoe (fol. 18b); *color illustration, page 16*

Chapter 1 **Introduction by Ibn al-Muqaffa**

Fols. 19a–26a; figs. 7–11

Ibn al-Muqaffa describes the merits of the work and includes several parenthetical stories to illustrate his points. He states, for example, that reading the book without attaining knowledge and making this knowledge profitable is like the story of the man who discovers a treasure and foolishly hires others to carry it; they walk off with the treasure and the man is left empty-handed. Other stories involve the young scholar who memorizes a phrase without understanding its meaning and uses it out of context in the presence of learned men; the man who pretends to be sleeping while a thief enters his house but becomes drowsy and really falls asleep; the man who steals the shirt of the thief who has come to deprive him of his possessions; and the merchant who steals his own share of goods thinking that it belongs to his partner.

Ibn al-Muqaffa concludes the introduction with a statement summarizing the aim of the book. He writes that the author of the book had four objectives in mind when he composed the work: to render it attractive to the young reader by employing birds and animals in the stories; to capture the attention of rulers by the conduct of the animals who are faced with similar dilemmas and circumstances; to provide entertainment to all peoples and to arouse their curiosity, thereby enabling the book to be preserved through the ages; and to provide the philosophers of the future a forum for discussion and speculation.

Fig. 8. The Young Scholar before Learned Men (fol. 21b)

Fig. 7. The Man Who Discovered the Treasure Has It Carried by Laborers (fol. 20b)

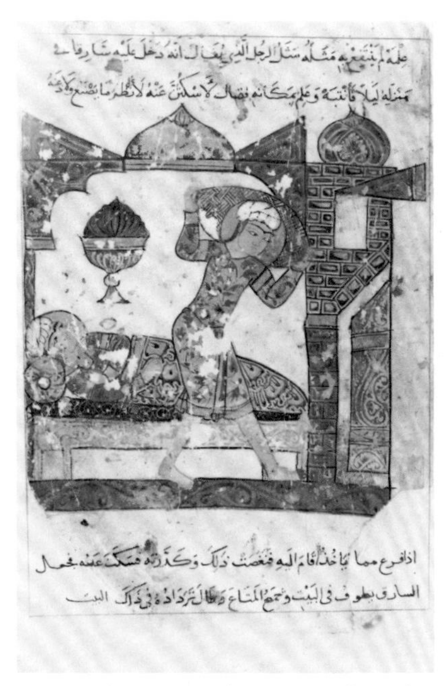

Fig. 9. The Man Who Pretends to be Asleep While the Thief Enters His House (fol. 22a)

Fig. 10. The Merchant and His Partner Carrying Goods (fol. 24a)

Fig. 11. The Man Apprehending the Thief (fol. 25a)

Chapter 2 **The Biography of Burzoe**
Fols. 26a–37a; figs. 12–16

This chapter, placed before the book proper as requested by Burzoe, is thought to have been written not by Buzurjmihr, the minister, but by Burzoe himself. It includes too much personal data and excursions into Burzoe's inner self and his search for the true religion to have been composed by a second person. Buzurjmihr may have rearranged the material supplied by Burzoe or merely lent his name to the biography written by the physician. It may also have been doctored by Ibn al-Muqaffa.

Burzoe, a man of good birth and education, studies medicine and attains knowledge. He begins to ponder the value of worldly gains and to treat the sick without monetary compensation. He searches for the true religion; finding none totally convincing and purely spiritual, he becomes an ascetic. Burzoe is assigned to obtain the *Kalila wa Dimna* from India and returns to Iran with many ancient books, including this work.

Burzoe's biography includes stories illustrating his discourses. His fear of trusting and believing and then being let down is symbolized by the tale of the thieves who try to rob the house of a rich man but slip and fall into the bedroom. Burzoe is afraid to wrong himself like the young man who became the lover of a married woman, was caught by her husband, and was badly beaten. Another soul-searching excursion leads to the tale of the workman who spends the day idly playing cymbals and cannot earn his daily wages from the merchant. Burzoe writes that weakness in humans is allegorized by the man who falls into a well or deep pit while fleeing from a wild elephant. He steps on two snakes and while hovering over the pit, holds onto withered branches gnawed by mice. At the bottom of the well is a dragon with an open mouth, ready to devour him. The man gluttonously reaches for the honey in a beehive in one of the trees, loses his foothold, and falls to his death.

Fig. 12. Thieves Entering the Bedroom of the Rich Man (fol. 30a)

Fig. 13. One of the Thieves Falling into the Bedroom and Being Caught (fol. 31a)

Fig. 14. The Husband Beating his Wife's Lover (fol. 32a)

Fig. 15. The Merchant Listening to the Workman Playing Cymbals (fol. 33a)

Fig. 16. The Man taking Refuge in a Well Inhabited by a Dragon (fol. 36b)

Chapter 3 **The Lion and the Ox**

Fols. 37a–69a; figs. 17–33

This chapter, the longest and the most profusely illustrated section in the book, is the beginning of the original *Kalila wa Dimna.* The story, taken from the *Panchatantra,* is about friendship, mistrust, and treachery; it is meant to counsel rulers to work out their own problems and not rely on the advice on ministers. The events revolve around the court of the lion, which includes two jackals, Kalila and Dimna. Dimna, who aspires to higher rank in the court, helps the lion overcome his fear of the ox, who eventually becomes the boon companion of the lion. Dimna is jealous of this friendship and finds his influence with the lion replaced by that of the ox. He resorts to treachery, telling each that the other is about to kill him. They believe these lies and engage in a long fight, at the end of which the lion kills the ox.

This parable contains numerous tales within tales told by the characters, including the story of the fox and the drum, which illustrates that not everyone who makes noise is dangerous. The stories of the rams and the ascetic and of the owner of the brothel who tries to poison the lover of her favorite courtesan but is herself killed in the process prove that greed does not always pay. The complicated affairs of the shoemaker, the barber, and their wives are resolved by truth. The tale of the crab and the heron and that of the lion and the hare teach that one should not trust the enemy. The fable of the three fish and the fishermen illustrates the detrimental results of procrastination. The parable of the lion, the crow, the wolf, the jackal, and the camel cautions against foolishness and conspiracy among friends. The story of the geese and the tortoise teaches the importance of listening to wise counsel. The tale of the monkeys and the glowworm shows that only the wise and prudent can be taught. The story of the simpleton and the rogue illustrates that the crafty person often falls into his own snare.

Fig. 17. Kalila and Dimna Conversing (fol. 40b)

Fig. 18. Dimna with Two Lions (fol. 41b)

Fig. 19. The Fox and the Drum (fol. 43b); *color illustration, page 19*

Fig. 20. Dimna with the Lion and the Ox (fol. 45a); *color illustration, page 20*

Fig. 21. The Ascetic Watching Two Butting Rams and the Fox (fol. 46a)

Fig. 22. The Ascetic Watching the Woman Trying to Poison the Lover (fol. 46b)

Fig. 24. The Crab and the Heron (fol. 50a)

Fig. 26. Three Fish and the Fishermen (fol. 53a)

Fig. 23. The Ascetic before the Judge with the Barber and His Wife (fol. 48a)

Fig. 25. The Hare and the Lion (fol. 51b); *color illustration, page 22*

Fig. 27. The Lion and the Elephant Fighting (fol. 58b); *color illustration, page 24*

Fig. 28. The Lion, the Crow, the Wolf, and the Jackal Attacking the Camel (fol. 60a); *color illustration, page 25*

Fig. 30. The Lion and the Ox Fighting (fol. 63a); *color illustration, page 28*

Fig. 32. The Birds and the Monkeys with the Glowworm (fol. 65b)

Fig. 29. Two Geese Carrying the Tortoise (fol. 61b); *color illustration, page 27*

Fig. 31. Kalila and Dimna Conversing (fol. 64b)

Fig. 33. The Rogue's Father Emerging from the Tree (fol. 67a)

Chapter 4 **The Trial of Dimna**
Fols. 69a–81a; figs. 34–38

This chapter was added by Ibn al-Muqaffa to the original *Kalila wa Dimna*. At the end of the story of the lion and the ox, Dimna, who caused the death of the ox by his deceit and lies, goes unpunished and becomes a minister at the court. Ibn al-Muqaffa's additional chapter provides the moral conclusion and presents the justice due to the cunning jackal; it includes Dimna's trial, defense, imprisonment, and eventual death by starvation. This chapter is essentially the conclusion of the tales of Kalila and Dimna. Although the book is named after them, ensuing stories have nothing to do with the two jackals.

In addition to the lengthy trial and defense, the chapter contains parenthetical stories, including a fable about the peasant and his two scantily dressed wives, which illustrates that a person should not judge another's shame without evaluating his own; and the tale of the falcon who plucks out the eyes of the false witness, which proves that he who bears witness to what his eyes have not seen and relates what his ears have not heard will be punished.

Fig. 34. The Lion with His Mother (fol. 70a); *color illustration, page 30*

Fig. 36. The Leopard Addressing the Army (fol. 75b)

Fig. 35. Kalila Visiting the Imprisoned Dimna (fol. 73b); *color illustration, page 31 and frontispiece*

Fig. 37. The Peasant with His Two Wives (fol. 77b)

Fig. 38. The Falcon Plucking out the Eyes of the False Witness (fol. 80b)

Chapter 5 **The Ringdove**
Fols. 81a–93a; figs. 39–42

This parable, which is devoted to brotherhood and friendship among the crow, the mouse, the tortoise, and the gazelle, is also from the *Panchatantra*. It forms a counterpart to the story of the lion and the ox, which illustrates the effects of treachery and corruption on friendship and shows how creatures of different species can depend on one another's help and compassion.

One of the stories told by Zirak, the mouse, narrates how he used to jump into a basket of food in the ascetic's house and have a fine meal, depriving the owner of his own food. Zirak gives up this habit when he sees the ascetic's guest steal his host's belongings; the mouse moves to the country and vows to lead a righteous life.

Fig. 39. The Mouse Gnawing the Net Imprisoning the Doves (fol. 82b); *color illustration, page 34*

Fig. 40. The Ascetic with His Guest (fol. 86a)

Fig. 41. The Gazelle with the Crow, the Mouse, and the Tortoise (fol. 90b); *color illustration, page 36*

Fig. 42. The Gazelle Luring the Hunter While the Mouse Frees the Tortoise (fol. 92b); *color illustration, page 37*

Chapter 6 **The Owls and the Crows**

Fols. 93a–110b; figs. 43–51

This chapter, taken from the *Panchatantra,* cautions against trusting the enemy. It describes the war between the owls and the crows in which the crows outwit the owls and destroy them. Included in it is the tale of the hare and the elephant, which illustrates that cunning is more advantageous than might; the story of the carpenter, who disbelieved what he saw but believed the lies he heard while attempting to catch his wife with her lover; and the fable of the snake, who unwittingly bit the ascetic's son, became feeble as the result of a curse, and in the end was befriended by the frogs, which teaches compassion for one's enemies.

Fig. 43. The Owls Attacking the Crows (fol. 94a); *color illustration, page 39*

Fig. 44. The King of the Crows Addressing His Subjects (fol. 94b)

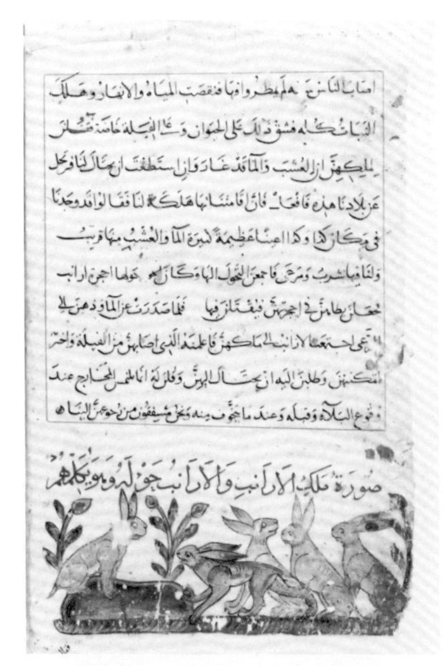

Fig. 45. The King of the Hares Addressing His Subjects (fol. 97b)

Fig. 46. Fairuz, the Hare, Addressing the Hares (fol. 98a); *color illustration, page 41 and cover*

Fig. 47. Fairuz at the Pond with the King of the Elephants (fol. 99a); *color illustration, page 42*

Fig. 48. The Crow Talking to the King of the Owls (fol. 102b); *color illustration, page 44*

Fig. 49. The Husband Hiding under the Bed to Observe His Wife (fol. 104b)

Fig. 50. The Crows Trapping the Owls in the Cave (fol. 107a); *color illustration, page 45*

Fig. 51. The Ascetic's Son Being Bitten by the Snake (fol. 108b)

Chapter 7 **The Monkey and the Tortoise**

Fols. 110b–117b; figs. 52–56

The purpose of this story, originally from the *Panchatantra,* is to teach rulers to value and protect their possessions and not let them slip away. It is illustrated by the story of the friendship between the monkey and the tortoise in which the tortoise by his cunning loses the trust of the monkey and ends up disappointed and friendless.

Included in this section is the short story of the ascetic and the weasel (fols. 116a–117b), which is often a separate chapter in the *Kalila wa Dimna.* Also from the *Panchatantra,* this story demonstrates that the man who is hasty in his decisions and acts without examining causes and consequences is bound to lose. The parable involves a story within a story and narrates the tale of the ascetic who broke his jar containing honey and oil while daydreaming of the profits these goods would bring him. Included in the parable is the story of the ascetic who inadvertently kills the weasel, not knowing that it was the weasel who saved his infant son from the snake.

Three paintings illustrate the story of the monkey and the tortoise, while two are devoted to the tale of the ascetic and the weasel. In the last scene, the snake and the weasel are sketched in but not painted.

Fig. 52. The Monkey Dropping Figs to the Tortoise (fol. 111b)

Fig. 53. The Tortoise Swimming with the Monkey on His Back (fol. 114a); *color illustration, page 47*

Fig. 54. The Monkey Jumping Safely to the Shore (fol. 114b); *color illustration, page 48*

Fig. 55. The Ascetic Hitting the Jar (fol. 116b)

Fig. 56. The Ascetic Finding His Son Alive in the Crib (fol. 117a)

Chapter 8 **The Wise Bilar and Queen Ilar**

Fols. 117b–130a; figs. 57–62

This parable, taken from an unknown Indian source, cautions against hasty decisions, similar to the message of the previous chapter, and teaches rulers to trust wise counsel. The king has several dreams, which are interpreted by the Brahmans to suit their own purposes and to avenge 12,000 of their members whose deaths had been ordered by the king. His queen, Ilar, suggests that he consult the ascetic Kinayrun, who reinterprets the dreams to mean that the king will receive many gifts. When the gifts arrive, the queen's rival chooses a golden garment that excites the king; the queen, angered at his reaction, throws a bowl of rice at the king. This infuriates the king, who orders her execution by Bilar, his confidant and minister. Bilar hides the queen and tells the king several tales, which teach that a sensible man should not punish hastily.

One of these stories is about the doves who fill their nest with wheat and barley while the grains are wet. When summer comes, the grains dry and shrink. The cock accuses his mate of eating the missing portion and pecks her to death. When the rains come and the grains swell, he realizes his mistake, refuses to eat or drink, and perishes at her side.

The king repents his hasty decision and bemoans the loss of his beloved queen; he rejoices when Bilar produces the queen, who is alive and well. At the end of the story the deceitful Brahmans are put to death.

Fig. 58. Queen Ilar Throwing a Bowl of Rice at the King (fol. 123b)

Fig. 60. The King with His Minister Bilar (fol. 125b)

Fig. 57. The King with the Ascetic Kinayrun (fol. 121a)

Fig. 59. Two Doves Fighting in Their Grain-Filled Nest (fol. 125a)

Fig. 61. Bilar Showing Ilar to the King (fol. 129a)

Fig. 62. The Execution of the Brahmans (fol. 130a)

Fig. 63. The Mouse Gnawing the Net Confining the Cat (fol. 131b); *color illustration, page 51*

Fig. 64. The King with the Philosopher (fol. 133a)

Chapter 9 **The Mouse and the Cat**
Fols. 130a–133b; fig. 63

One of the three short stories taken from the *Mahabharata* included in the book teaches that although during times of distress enemies can become friends, they must resume their own lives when conditions change. It is enacted by a cat who is caught in a net and is befriended by a mouse who frees him. Since the cat and the mouse are natural enemies, they part.

Chapter 10 **The King and the Bird**
Fols. 133b–136a; figs. 64–66

This story, also from the *Mahabharata,* teaches rulers to guard against vindictiveness. It involves the king and a fabulous talking bird called Fanzah. When the bird's young is killed by the jealous prince, Fanzah avenges his death by tearing out the eyes of the prince with her claws. The king tries to trick her into coming back so that he can punish her, but the bird fears his revenge and flies away.

Fig. 65. The Prince Killing the Young Bird (fol. 133b)

Fig. 66. The Mother Bird Tearing out the Eyes of the Prince (fol. 134a)

Fig. 67. The King with the Philosopher (fol. 136b)

Fig. 69. The Lion with the Jackal and Wolves (fol. 142b)

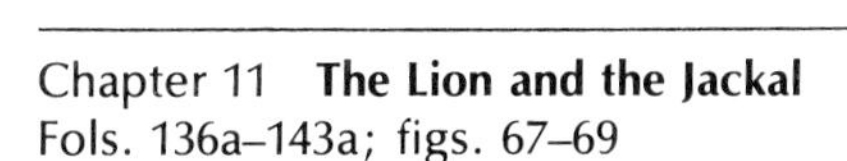

Chapter 11 **The Lion and the Jackal**
Fols. 136a–143a; figs. 67–69

Another short story from the *Mahabharata* teaches that man should be reconciled with those he has mistreated. An ascetic jackal, who eats no flesh, becomes a steward in the court of the lion. The jealous wolves and jackals plot against the jackal by hiding the lion's meat in his house. When it is discovered, the lion orders the jackal's execution. The lion's mother counsels him to seek the truth; the plot is unveiled and the jackal is restored to office.

Fig. 68. The Lion and the Jackal (fol. 138b)

Chapter 12 **The Traveler and the Jeweler**
Fols 143a–146a; figs. 70–73

The parable of the man who is good to the unworthy is derived from an unknown Indian source. The jeweler, the monkey, the leopard, and the snake, who have all fallen into a pit, are saved by a traveling ascetic. In time, the animals repay his kindness, but the jeweler falsely accuses the ascetic of murder. The truth is finally revealed and the jeweler is punished.

The last folio in this chapter has been bound in reverse; the parade of the discredited ascetic should precede the execution of the jeweler.

Fig. 70. The King with the Philosopher (fol. 143a)

Fig. 71. The Ascetic Freeing the Jeweler from the Pit (fol. 144b); *color illustration, page 53*

Fig. 72. The Execution of the Jeweler (fol. 145a)

Fig. 73. The Discredited Ascetic Paraded Backward on a Donkey (fol. 145b)

Chapter 13 **The Prince and His Companions**

Fols 146a–149a; figs. 74–75

This chapter, which demonstrates the inevitability of the will of God, is also from an unknown Indian legend. The story is about a prince and his three companions who go into a town and by their individual abilities try to attain wealth. The son of the farmer uses labor and toil; the son of the nobleman uses his good looks and benefits from the attentions of a rich man's wife; the son of the merchant gains from trade; and the prince becomes the king of the town.

Fig. 74. The King with the Philosopher (fol. 146a)

Fig. 75. The New King Riding through the Town (fol. 148a)

Chapter 14 **The Lioness and the Horseman**
Fols. 149a–151a; figs. 76–77

A fourth story from an unidentified Indian source involves the lioness who finds her cubs killed and skinned by the horseman. She renounces the eating of flesh and lives on plants and fruit, realizing from her own experience what grief is caused by the killing of animals.

Fig. 76. The Lioness Finds Her Cubs Killed and Skinned (fol. 150a)

Fig. 77. The Lioness Eats Plants, Having Forsaken Meat (fol. 150b)

Chapter 15 **The Ascetic and His Guest**
Fols. 151a–152a; fig. 78

This story, thought to have been added to the *Kalila wa Dimna* by Ibn al-Muqaffa, is of Near Eastern origin. It teaches that if a man abandons his craft for another, he will forget the first without having mastered the second. The story involves a traveler who visits the ascetic and wants to learn his language. The ascetic replies that if the traveler gives up his own language and tries to learn another, he would be like the crow who imitated the walk of the partridge, forgot his own gait, and kept stumbling.

Fig. 78. The Crow Imitating the Partridge (fol. 151b)

Bibliography

General Works

Brockelmann, C. "Kalilah wa-Dimnah." *Encyclopedia of Islam,* 2d ed., vol. 4, pp. 503–6. Leiden: E. J. Brill; London: Luzac & Co., 1978.

Keith-Falconer, Ion G. N. *Kalilah and Dimnah, or the Fables of Bidpai.* Amsterdam: Philo Press, 1970 (reprint of Cambridge: Cambridge University Press, 1885).

Knatchbull, Wyndham. *Kalila and Dimna, or the Fables of Bidpai.* Oxford: W. Baxter, 1819.

Wollaston, Arthur N. *The Anwar-i Suhaili, or the Lights of Canopus.* London: John Murray, 1904.

Wood, Ramsey. *Kalila and Dimna: Selected Fables of Bidpai.* New York: Alfred A. Knopf, 1980.

The Bodleian Manuscript

Arnold, Thomas W. *Painting in Islam.* New York: Dover Publications, 1965 (reprint of Oxford: Clarendon Press, 1928), pl. LXIIIa.

Atıl, Esin. *Renaissance of Islam: Art of the Mamluks.* Washington, D.C.: Smithsonian Institution Press, 1981, no. III, figs. 9–12.

Aziatische Miniaturen. Delft: Museum het Prinsenhof, 1967, pl. 13.

Binyon, Laurence; Wilkinson, J. V. S.; and Gray, Basil. *Persian Miniature Painting.* New York: Dover Publications, 1971 (reprint of London: Oxford University Press, 1933), no. 4, pls. IIIA–B and IVA–B.

Buchthal, Hugo. "Indian Fables in Islamic Art." *Journal of the Royal Asiatic Society* (1941): 317–24, fig. 2.

Catalogue of the International Exhibition of Persian Art. London: Royal Academy of Arts, 1931, no. 534C.

Diringer, David. *The Illuminated Book: Its History and Production.* New York and Washington, D.C.: Frederick A. Praeger, 1967, pl. III-5.c.

Ettinghausen, Richard. *Arab Painting.* Geneva: Albert Skira, 1962, p. 154.

Gray, Basil. *Persian Painting.* London: E. Benn Ltd., 1930, pl. 2.

Haldane, Duncan. *Mamluk Painting*. Warminster, England: Aris & Phillips, Ltd., 1978, pp. 85–86.

Holter, Kurt. "Die frühmamlukische Miniaturenmalerei." *Die Graphischen Künste* 2 (1937): 1–14.

———. "Die Galen-Handschrift und die Makamen des Harîrî der Wiener Nationalbibliothek." *Jahrbuch der Kunsthistorischen Sammlungen in Wien,* n.s. 9, special no. 104 (1937): 1–48.

James, David. "Arab Painting." *Marg* 29, no. 3 (June 1976): 8–50, fig. 19.

Mayer, L. A. *Mamluk Costume: A Survey*. Geneva: Albert Kundig, 1952, pl. XVII:1–2.

Walzer, Sofie. "An Illustrated Leaf from a Lost Mamluk Kalilah wa-Dimnah Manuscript." *Ars Orientalis* 2 (1957): 503–5.

———. "The Mamluk Illuminated Manuscripts of Kalila wa-Dimna." In *Aus der Welt der Islamischen Kunst: Festschrift für Ernst Kühnel,* edited by Richard Ettinghausen, pp. 195–206, figs. 2, 6, 10, 14, and 18. Berlin: Verlag Gebr. Mann, 1959.

This book was produced by the Smithsonian Institution Press, Washington, D.C.
The type is VIP Optima set by Monotype Composition Co., Inc., Baltimore. The paper is eighty-pound Warren's Lustro Offset Enamel Dull text and cover, with Colortext endsheets. *The cloth is B-grade Holliston Roxite stamped with foil.*
Printed by Garamond-Pridemark Press, Baltimore. Designed by Elizabeth Sur.